CHAIN REACTIONS

David Neal Keller

CHAIN REACTIONS

THE LIFE
OF
WILFRED R. KONNEKER

OHIO UNIVERSITY SPECIAL PUBLICATIONS

ATHENS

Ohio University Special Publications, Athens, Ohio 45701
© 2003 by Ohio University Special Publications
Printed in the United States of America

Ohio University Special Publications books are printed on acid-free paper ♾

11 10 09 08 07 06 05 04 03   5 4 3 2 1

Library of Congress Cataloging-in-Publication Data
Keller, David Neal.
   Chain reactions : the life of Wilfred R. Konneker / David Neal Keller.
      p. cm.
   Includes bibliogaphical references and index.
   ISBN: 0-9667644-3-9 (cloth : alk. paper)
   1. Konneker, Wilfred R. (Wilfred Rudolph), 1922– 2. Nuclear medicine—Ohio—
Biography. 3. Businesspeople—Ohio—Biography. 4. Philanthropists—Ohio—Biography.
I. Title.

R895.K66K427 2003
616.07'575'092—dc22
   [B]

2003056312

CONTENTS

ACKNOWLEDGMENTS

Compiling biographic material about a dynamic person with wide-ranging interests and accomplishments obviously requires the cooperation of a great many participants willing to share thoughts and information with the author. In this instance, such contributions came from so many individuals and groups that it would be unrealistic to attempt a listing without slighting many whose help is greatly appreciated. Family members, friends, faculty, and administrators at Ohio University and Washington University in St. Louis, public librarians, and business and civic associates of Wilfred Konneker certainly head the list.

It does seem appropriate, however, to single out several people who coordinated research efforts, sometimes providing personal assistance in obtaining information. Margaret Sheskey, assistant vice president, administration, of Ohio University, helped coordinate the overall project. Carole Prietto, archivist of Washington University, researched a variety of materials there. Sue Ann Baird, a member of the administrative staff at Greenfield Exempted Village Schools, helped locate information during and after the author's visits to McClain High School. Jane Greenwalt, public affairs officer of the U.S. Department of Energy's Miamisburg (Ohio) Environmental Management Project, located detailed data on the Dayton phase of the Manhattan Project. Cathy Fraser of Olean, New York, served as a correspondent for that city. Susan Joyce checked records of Springfield Lake Sanitarium and its Sunshine Cottage. Sue Winter, executive secretary of Konneker Development, Inc., played an integral cooperative role throughout the project. My wife, Marian, provided proofreading and editorial suggestions that were invaluable, as always.

PROLOGUE

In a nation known to esteem accomplishments of the scientist, the entrepreneur, and the philanthropist, it is unusual to find all three callings combined in a single persona. Seasoned with a dash of Horatio Algerism and a leveling portion of self-effacing humor, the mixture can be worthy of recognition as a truly American biography.

Wilfred R. Konneker proved to be a consummate entrepreneur immediately after receiving a Ph.D. in nuclear physics, by rejecting existing career paths to create a business that had no precedent. He became a philanthropist without thinking of his action as such, simply because he believed it would contribute to the cause of education, which he considered vital to the future health of humankind. After uncommon success in diagnostic nuclear medicine, he saw biology as a possible base for a private business at a time when it was considered only a subject for research and teaching. In doing so, he became just as excited in starting something to profit others as he had been when he was building his own business. As he moved forward in creating new ventures, he never seemed to erase friendships and experiences of the past, but rather added them to his repertoire without becoming overwhelmed. Events of the past blended comfortably into those of the present and plans for the future.

No one who knew Will well contested his assertion that the most important accomplishment of his life was convincing Ann Lee Hancock to become his wife. This book, in truth, might more appropriately be considered a "duography," if only the word existed.

Myriad writings during nearly the entire history of the United States have well established its leadership in philanthropy. Alexis de Tocqueville, the visiting French aristocrat whose two-volume *Democracy in America* became an icon of sociological insight, recognized it in the 1830s. Fifty years later, famed British journalist James Boyce wrote, "In works of beneficence, no country has surpassed, perhaps none has equaled the United States."

Toward the end of the twentieth century, Daniel J. Boorstin, Pulitzer Prize–winning author, historian, and director emeritus of the Library of Congress, reiterated this role of voluntary collaborative activities in America from the beginning.

The report of a national Commission on Private Philanthropy and Public Needs concluded that "money gifts" and the contributions of volunteer time and labor are "sizable forces in American Society, far larger than in any other country," and have "contributed immeasurably to this country's social and scientific progress."

Higher education and the performing arts often are listed at or near the top of important social treasures that become increasingly dependent on such private giving. If it depended solely on ticket sales, even the Metropolitan Opera, with its consistent sell-out attendance, would lose $30,000 "each time it raises the curtain," according to an assistant manager. Community orchestras and theatrical groups that once could focus only on performances now include a wealth of ongoing educational programs for children and adults, as well as tours to outlying locations. Requirements for quality higher education, beyond public support and student fees, have become so well documented that they need no explication. These also happen to be the two major areas of philanthropic support Will and Ann Lee Konneker chose to embrace.

This book, however, is not intended to be a treatise on the cause of philanthropy. It is the story of a man who rose from what could have been a justifiable source of discouragement, met the challenges of life without considering obstacles to be barriers, married a young lady with a similar philosophy, and enjoyed a never-ending quest toward new objectives, several of which involved sparking chain reactions in the support of education and the arts.

PART I

FRAMEWORK FOR INGENUITY

One essential to success is that your desire be an all-obsessing one, your thoughts and aims be coordinated, and your energy be concentrated and applied without letup.

—ANONYMOUS

1

A DAY IN MARCH

*You can make more friends in two months
by becoming interested in other people than
you can in two years by trying to get other
people interested in you.*

—DALE CARNEGIE

March weather in St. Louis is likely to bounce frequently and unpredictably between frigid and balmy, as if it were trying to determine, as do many residents, whether the city should be identified with the North or the South. Western winds still delivering heavy snows to Chicago and farther east during the fading days of winter often sweep by Missouri's largest metropolis, barely grazing its diverse suburbs, as though they formed a climatic dividing line.

March 30, 1996, was one of the mild days. Fifty-four-degree weather greeted Wilfred and Ann Lee Konneker just before sunset, when they left their ranch-style house in suburban Ladue, drove around the circular driveway to Barclay Woods, and headed their Rolls Royce toward the home of their daughter and her family, seven miles to the west. It had been an unusual Saturday, not just because it was the day before their fiftieth wedding anniversary, but because they had spent a large part of it at Facade Limited, a five-star spa where each had been pampered with a massage, whirlpool, hot tub, manicure, and pedicure. Although it was something they had never experienced before, they could hardly refuse the special treatment. It was an anniversary present from an insistent daughter, who made all of the arrangements, including driving them to and from the spa. Ann Lee's program also included a hairdo and facial, but her husband adamantly rejected those phases of the afternoon's adventure, daughter or no daughter.

As they approached their destination in the suburb of Town and Country, where a family dinner would complete the day's events, they didn't question the novelty of their present, nor the fact that the dinner was being held a day before their actual anniversary. Neither did they reflect on the trip abroad they had discussed for the occasion more than six months earlier, nor recall that their only child had convinced them that she, her husband, and their two children would be disappointed if they were away at such an important time. Frequent travelers, they had been happy to forgo another excursion in favor of celebrating at home with daughter B. Lynn Webster, her husband, Bill, and their small children, Cara and "Trey."

The Websters had moved into their home on Topping Woods Estates Drive two years earlier when the attractive residential subdivision was created from what had been farm fields, woods, and a stone quarry. Their two-story brick home with twin front pillars was located on a one-acre lot. An example of the city's fast growth was indicated by high-rise office buildings going up in an adjoining suburb, Des Peres, altering the background, which previously had been tree-lined. There was sufficient separation, however, to avoid interfering with the tranquility of the Topping area, a montage of individual neighborhoods, where emphasis was placed on preservation of trees, green space, and wildlife to maintain a pastoral setting. Town and Country, some twelve miles from downtown St. Louis, had a population of eight thousand. It had grown eightfold since being incorporated in 1950 and was continuing to expand, as were other metropolitan and suburban areas of the city with the Gateway Arch.

The sun had just dipped beneath the skyline, adding a calm finale to the relaxing afternoon, as Will and Ann Lee turned into the Webster driveway and parked. But when they were greeted at the door by their family, mysteries concerning the spa and events of previous months quickly became unveiled. In the entranceway and adjoining great room stood a smiling group of family members and closest friends from several parts of the country, each of whom had been important in their lives, from childhood, through school days, business careers, cultural, educational, and civic philanthropic endeavors, social affiliations, and worldwide travels. B. Lynn, with help from Sue Winter, Will's longtime confidential secretary, had spent well over a year preparing this golden anniversary reunion, including soliciting photographs in advance, then arranging for out-of-towners to fly or drive to the city and stay at the nearby Marriott West Hotel. B. Lynn had made certain she could monitor her parents' whereabouts—not a minor accomplishment—by sequestering them at the spa, while all guests congregated at the hotel and rode to her home in a bus, which then departed, leaving no telltale vehicle in sight.

The initial surprise continued to unfold as the honorees greeted celebrants from Florida, New Jersey, Ohio, Kansas, and Missouri. Furniture had been removed from the two-story great room, replaced with circular tables decorated with flowers, candles, ribbons, and coverings, all conforming to a gold motif. Plants, streamers, and other decorations surrounded the large fireplace and lined the walls. A combo on the second-floor balcony, ordinarily the family's computer center, played big band music from the forties and fifties.

As the dinner hour approached, landmark events of the honorees' lives were chronicled in champagne toasts, some more appropriately described as roasts, offered by the guests.

Winona Conley, Will's sister and only sibling, revealed humorous incidents of teenage years when they were growing up in the village of Greenfield, Ohio. Twice widowed and retired from a career in teaching, she now lived with a son and his wife in Tallahassee, Florida, but the man she referred to as her "little brother" remained close through correspondence and frequent visits.

Jane Edwards, Ann Lee's older sister, was prompted by music from the balcony to recall how the two loved dancing in their hometown of Olean, New York, "where jitterbugging was the favorite recreational pastime of the community." Also a widow and former teacher, she had flown in from Bradenton, Florida, where she lived during the winter months, alternating with summers spent at the renowned Chautauqua Institution resort in southwestern New York State.

Ed Hope's boyhood friendship with Will began in Greenfield and extended on through the years when he married a young Scottish lady, Jean Faull, progressed through a diversified career in education, concluding it as superintendent of schools in his hometown, and retired in Dublin, Ohio, a suburb of Columbus. Ann Lee also became a close friend of the Hopes from the time they were married, and the two couples had since managed to be together regularly, despite living four hundred miles apart.

Robert and Phyliss Allen met Will and Ann Lee as suburban neighbors in the mid-fifties. "Bob was a lawyer and Will was developing his nuclear business, and we were all young," Phyliss said. "We were happy, struggling pioneers together," Robert added, "and we socialized more and more into a friendship that remains just as strong today." As their careers developed, Robert Allen also represented the Konnekers in several legal matters.

Jan Boehm and Ann Lee became acquainted through the St. Louis alumna chapter of Chi Omega sorority. A spin-off group from the organization kept them together in a bridge club, which they expanded into a social circle admitting husbands and meeting regularly for half a century. Jan's husband, Elmer, a Monsanto executive, in fact, became the unofficial social chairman. Known as "The Bridgers," even after they abandoned card playing in favor of socializing, the group did so many family things together that their children developed a second generation of lasting friendships.

Mel and Mildred Dold, who drove to the anniversary party from their home in Wichita, Kansas, also met Will and Ann Lee in the 1950s, when the four of them became rivals, then partners in a compelling avocation: competitive dog showing. Traveling separately around the country and entering their animals in leading shows, the Dolds and Konnekers soon were traveling together, with their children, on family vacations.

Barbara Pond, a valued employee in the formative years of Will's major company, had lived for a short time with the Konnekers and had been influential in suggesting the distinctive naming of their daughter. She met her husband, Alexander, when he was a physics professor at Washington University in St. Louis, and they later moved to Long Island, where he became chairman of the Physics Department, then provost of the State University of New York at Stony Brook. Twenty years later he was named executive vice president and chief academic officer of Rutgers, the State University of New Jersey, before retiring to the Atlantic seashore village of Manasquam. The closeness of their friendship also remained undiminished by distance.

Charles Ping, who had retired two years earlier as president of Ohio

University, and his wife, Claire, continued to live in Athens, where both participated in academic and community affairs. For the past twenty years, they had been closely associated with Will and Ann Lee, as friends, traveling companions, and colleagues in university programs. These relationships were continuing to grow, with the two men sharing ongoing efforts in furthering what they considered to be America's most important objective: the education of its youth.

"Will doesn't just become active in projects that are important to him," Dr. Ping said. "He becomes totally committed. Our friendship was born out of a shared interest and allegiance to Ohio University, and then it became much more than that, and included our wives as well."

A similar dedication to progress of Washington University in St. Louis was evidenced in a later interview with Chancellor William Danforth, who noted, "Will is a person who believes strongly in the power of education, and he does everything he can to help further it. He is devoted to his wife and family, to the community he serves, and to the education of all young people."

As a philanthropist, Will Konneker was particularly notable in that he donated an extraordinary amount of time and effort, as well as substantial resources, to a wide variety of interests. "Some people in philanthropy give money and leave it at that," said David Blassingame, Washington University vice chancellor for alumni and development programs. "Will is not that way; he puts his heart and soul into things, and he does anything that needs to be done, whether it is big or small."

Long after retirement, "Dr. K," as Will often was called, continued to arrive at his office by 9 A.M. each day that he was in St. Louis, spending hours raising money by telephone for worthy causes, most of them associated with education and arts, attending board and committee meetings of such groups, and answering calls from company leaders seeking his advice, breaking away periodically for meetings with colleagues in various independent business ventures. A familiar figure on the campus of Washington University, he chaired committees, served on boards, and worked with special advisory groups. Away from the city, he was often to be found working with similar organizations—always without pay—particularly those at Ohio University.

The consensus among those whose lives he touched regularly was astonishment at his unassuming manner of accomplishing so many things without seeming to realize the uncommonness of it all. When he was helping promote a symphony, opera, or other performing arts group, that seemed to become the major focus of his passion. On his favorite topic of higher education and how it can and must be extended to as many deserving people as possible, and how important it is to solving the world's problems, it was difficult to realize one was talking to a scientist-entrepreneur. Yet his worldwide professional reputation had been achieved as a nuclear physicist who pioneered a field of diagnostic medicine previously considered strictly a branch of research and parlayed it into a thriving business. Thomas Wagner, a former university-based colleague who later directed an important oncology research institute, once stated, "If Dr. Konneker's main interest had been philosophy, he would have managed somehow to form a successful philosophy company."

A great many persons through the years attempted to identify the motivations inspiring Will Konneker to attain heights that would have seemed to be out of reach for a person with his start in life. Perhaps the consensus of those who knew him best was expressed by Robert Glidden, Dr. Ping's successor as president of Ohio University:

> I think Will Konneker is the ideal combination of scholar and entrepreneur. He is a research scientist who continues to be intrigued and thrilled by that whole process. At the same time, he has been successful in taking those ideas and making people's lives better, and incidentally making some money from it, which he then gives away. I think that whole process is exciting to Will and he simply wants to make more of it happen. He also is the kind of person who sees that things can be better with the right kind of help, both financial and otherwise, and isn't reluctant to dedicate his time to doing it. That is an attitude a few people have, and I think he is an outstanding example.

Will was known also for his ability to peer well into the future and devise ideas that would meet impending needs. Extremely patient, he rarely failed, because he kept persisting until he found ways to succeed. Incompetence and petulance privately perturbed him, but when he encountered either, he silently relegated the problem to his mental recycle bin and moved on without leaving a noticeable wake that might hurt feelings.

"When you meet Will, you like him, but if you know nothing about his background, you have no idea of what he can do, because he never tries to impress you," said Jack Ellis, a close friend who worked for Ohio University in matters that concerned them both. "Then you quickly discover he has a quiet assurance about himself and his relationship with family and friends. Trying to impress someone simply is not in his make-up. I think subconsciously he must feel, 'Accept me as I am, and if you do that's wonderful; if you don't that's your privilege.'"

Ellis and other good friends enjoyed chiding Will about his Rolls Royce, which seems incongruous with his heralded modesty. Was it his zest for top-quality machinery? Could it be attributed to a flair for the finer things in life? Was it a sudden impulse? The latter was highly unlikely in view of his having had three of them, beginning in 1982. Characteristically not allowing needling friends to put him in a defensive position, Will usually offered only a patent whimsical smile in response. But Ann Lee was quick to inject her stock answer. "Hey," she would say, "some husbands spend time playing golf, or tennis, or drinking, or carousing, or running around with other women. Mine likes nice cars."

After the wedding anniversary dinner, guests discovered why they had been asked to send photographs in advance, when they viewed a fast-moving memory-lane video presentation prepared by the Konnekers' son-in-law, Bill Webster, a professional videographer. The response confirmed what Will and Ann Lee repeated often and convincingly: with all that had happened in their busy lives, the most fulfilling attainments were the enduring friendships they enjoyed through the years.

2

A FAMILY TREE GROWS IN GREENFIELD

*What lies behind us and what lies ahead of us
are tiny matters compared with what lies
within us.*

—OLIVER WENDELL HOLMES

The course of Wilfred Konneker's childhood was altered abruptly at age four when his mother died of tuberculosis at Akron, Ohio, in July 1926. Despite worldwide research efforts, the dreaded airborne disease remained a medical mystery that had tormented communities for centuries. Consequently, "Will" and his seven-year-old sister, Winona, were taken from their father and placed in a Summit County sanitarium.

Roy Konneker, an Akron barber, did not want to send his children away, but he had no choice. Although scientists had been struggling to conquer the *Mycobacterium tuberculosis* during all of recorded history, the 1920s offered little hope for cure beyond rest, fresh air, good nutrition, and hope. These were provided most often at sanitariums, serving both infected patients and those considered by health departments to be at risk through close relationships with sufferers. Winona and Will Konneker obviously fit into the latter category; never mind the absence of symptoms.

The unrelenting affliction had led through the ages to a progression of desperate attempts to control it. More than four hundred years before the birth of Christ, Hippocrates of Cos had offered virtually the same treatment being followed in the twentieth century. The celebrated Greek physician referred to the disease as *pyhisis* and warned other doctors that treating advanced cases might damage their reputations because deaths would be inevitable.

Increasing understanding of problems and infectious characteristics developed gradually over the years, as the name changed to the white plague, then consumption, and finally tuberculosis, once the cause was identified as the spread of tubercle bacilli; yet the disease remained one of humanity's deadliest enemies. "Miracle" antibiotics and chemotherapy were not to appear until World War II, but even these would not prevent frequent epidemics from surfacing periodically into the twenty-first century, particularly in underdeveloped countries lacking sufficient public health care systems to control them.

So in 1926, prevention still was largely theoretical. One concept, originated by an Italian doctor who had cured himself by traveling to the Himalayan Mountains in the mid-1800s, was that the TB bacillus air delivery system made altitude important to treatment. His writings became instrumental in locating sanitariums, including the one where Roy Konneker's children were assigned.

Springfield Lake Sanitarium was constructed in 1915 on the highest point in Summit County, between Akron and Uniontown. Sunshine Cottage, for treatment of pediatric tuberculosis, subsequently was opened on the sanitarium grounds just four years before Will and Winona arrived. An attractive building, it had a fountain out front and plenty of space for playground equipment, toys, and even riding horses. With no medical treatment known at the time, children got good food, good air, good exercise, and plenty of sunshine.

For Will Konneker, such things became dim memories of being four years old. What would last, however, were general feelings of regimentation, loneliness, and extreme sadness that left indelible impressions of what he would understandably remember as "the worst time of my life." All he thought about at the time was returning to his father and maternal grandparents in Akron.

Being three years older, Winona was able to retain more of the details. Boys and girls lived in separate areas of Sunshine Cottage, so she and her little brother rarely saw each other. "I recall vividly that Will tried to run home whenever he had a chance," she said later, "and I learned they had to tie him to his bed to keep him there at times." Their father and grandparents were permitted to see them only during visiting hours.

Both Will and Winona eventually came to realize that unpleasant recollections of Sunshine Cottage were attributed to the nearly unbearable devastation of losing their mother and then being separated from their families, including each other. Decades later, on the extremely rare occasions when they could be enticed into reminiscing about the sanitarium, they emphasized that their emotions reflected in no way on the institution. Springfield Lake Sanitarium, renamed Edwin Shaw Hospital in 1934, evolved, in fact, into a highly respected complex with a proud history. It became the region's only comprehensive, fully accredited facility specializing in rehabilitation, with more than five hundred professionals and support staff treating inpatients and outpatients for a wide span of disorders and disabilities. Sunshine Cottage became Sunshine Village, built by the Summit County Child Welfare Board, with thirteen residential halls housing children who were orphaned or abused. In 1977 it was renamed Andersen Village.

After more than a year at Springfield Lake Sanitarium, Winona and Will Konneker were at last released to their father when it was determined officially that possible danger of exposure to the dreaded bacillus had been averted. For reasons not fully explained in records, Winona left in the summer of 1927, Will about six months later. But their mother's death had prompted family changes that soon relocated both children from Akron to Greenfield, Ohio, the birthplace of their father and the ancestral Konneker home for more than sixty years. This arrangement proved to be pivotal in cultivating the goals, career, and extraordinary loyalties that characterized Will Konneker's life.

In the sunset years of the eighteenth century, when America's young government was being led by George Washington, another surveyor destined for military and political fame was busy appraising a wilderness area of the "Ohio Country" that had been opened for white settlement by the 1795 Treaty of Greenville. Among the early accomplishments of twenty-seven-year-old Duncan McArthur was the 1799 founding of Greenfield, some twenty miles west of Chillicothe, another town he had helped lay out three years earlier, and the place where he made his home.

Four years later, Ohio became the nation's seventeenth state—the first carved out of the Northwest Territory—with Chillicothe its first capital. Greenfield, sometimes confused with the site of the famous treaty, had grown enough to have a church, a tavern, a mill, a rope factory, and its first school, the latter in the log-cabin home of a judge. Its name was as large as that of Cincinnati on the state's first engraved map.

McArthur's career soon led to the Ohio House of Representatives, the Senate, and, in 1830, the governorship. During a three-year sabbatical from politics, he also compiled a notable record in the war of 1812, rising to the rank of brigadier general and negotiating another treaty (in concert with Gov. Lewis Cass of Michigan Territory), this time ceding Ohio's remaining Native American lands to the United States. His acumen as a brilliant appraiser and shrewd buyer of desirable land made him one of the wealthiest property owners in the state.

As McArthur had predicted in early correspondence, rich soil in the rolling hills surrounding Greenfield soon attracted westward-moving farmers. Timber came down and cabins went up. A Greenfield writer noted, "Some of the settlers came on horseback, some on foot, some floated down the Ohio River on flatboats, but most of them came in Conestoga wagons, drawn by oxen. Early roads were in such bad condition that it was considered a load for a team of horses to haul about twenty-five bushels of grain." However primitive it may have seemed, the area gained official governmental stature when it became Highland County in 1805.

Greenfield itself grew in lockstep with other frontier farm communities, steadily, but with no aspiration of becoming a commercial hub like Cincinnati, its closest major neighbor eighty miles to the southwest. Fifty lots in the center of town were sold for $100 in 1812, but five years later, four lots brought a total of $750. That was one year after the first stagecoach arrived and eighteen years before the first covered bridge was built over Paint Creek, a wide, picturesque Scioto River tributary that bisected the town.

During the next few decades, large numbers of immigrants, a sizable percentage of them Germans seeking improved standards of living, swarmed into Ohio. The first wave, referred to as an "internal migration," came almost entirely from eastern states. Soon, however, their ranks were surpassed by others arriving directly from Europe. Many sought opportunities in the cities, but thousands funneled into villages and farms. The numbers swelled dramatically following a failed German revolution in 1848, and peaked in the 1860s when more than a third of all immigrants to the United States came from that country. Among them was young Henry W. Konneker, who arrived in 1868 at the age of eighteen, became a naturalized citizen at Cincinnati, and later moved inland to Greenfield. There he met Lucinda Fox, who had been born and reared in the town, and whose parents also were German immigrants. Henry and Lucinda were married in a Greenfield German Methodist church on November 3, 1875.

Like many other newcomers reportedly opposed to the rigid social class structure in authoritarian German states, Henry Konneker was a tradesman who aspired to be self-employed. As a result, he worked for a while as a stone cutter, then formed an independent coal delivery business in Green-field. Whether by example or mere coincidence, his self-determination might be interpreted as becoming ingrained in the Konneker lineage.

Ten children were born to Henry and Lucinda in the remaining years of the nineteenth century, the youngest, Roy George Konneker, arriving on July 27, 1896.

Described as "a well-rounded boy," Roy played varsity football and had what seemed to be a natural ability to play a variety of musical in-struments without formal instruction. Like three of his four older broth-ers, he also spent many of his nonschool hours learning the barbering trade from an old German who had a shop next to the Konneker Coal Company office. After graduating from high school in May of 1917, he decided to pursue a career in Akron, Ohio, a city enjoying rapid economic growth as the world's largest rubber manufacturing center. Working for a time in a tire plant, however, convinced him that self-employment would be more to his liking. Consequently, he opened a barbershop.

Some confusion exists concerning the first time Roy Konneker met a pretty young lady named Opal Barton, secretary to a vice president of the B. F. Goodrich Company. Nevertheless, correspondence and records show that after a brief courtship, they married on January 13, 1918, and built a home in the "Rubber City," where her mother and stepfather also lived.

Opal had been born in 1899 to John and Grace Hall Barton in Mount Vernon, Ohio, and reared in the small town of West Liberty, north of Greenfield. After her Irish immigrant father died of tuberculosis, her mother, whose ancestry was English, remarried Frank Standley and moved to Akron. A delicate, artistic woman, Opal was an excellent pianist and singer but chose to attend a business school in Highland County and enter the world of commerce. Goodrich was preparing her for a new position in Africa when she decided instead to become the wife of Roy Konneker.

The couple's first child, Winona, was born on January 13, 1919. Wilfred, named for uncles William and Frederick, followed on February 20, 1922. After Opal became ill with pneumonia, her mother and stepfather moved in with them to help with her care while Roy was at work in his barbershop and running an early-morning milk route. Medical knowledge at the time was insufficient to ascertain precisely how the young mother contracted the tuberculosis that took her life.

Faced with the dilemma of having no home, very little money, and wanting to chart the best possible course for his children's lives after the loss of their mother and the despair of confinement in a sanitarium, Roy Konneker turned to his family for a solution. Although close in terms of relationships, they were separated geographically. Only one unmarried sister, Olive, continued to live with their mother in Greenfield after the 1921 death of their father. Like Roy, all the others had moved.

Charles, the eldest brother, suffered severe nerve damage from birth, causing continuous hand tremors. Yet he graduated from the University of Michigan and became a highly successful architect and builder in Detroit, using a long pencil placed against his shoulder and chin to make drawings.

Frederick and William followed early inclinations to become barbers, also in Detroit. A man of versatile interests, Frederick learned cabinet making and horticulture, built homes, and served as a real estate broker while continuing to operate his barbershop in the shadow of the General Motors and Fisher Buildings. Ralph entered the army in World War I, serving as an airplane mechanic helping the bi-wing fighters stay aloft in Europe—an unusual challenge at that point in aviation—and later opened an automobile garage in Akron.

The eldest sibling, Gertrude, born in 1877, married Virgil Vance in April 1900 but died of polio the following July. Nell moved West and married. Grace, who became Mrs. Harry Dreyer in 1920, lived in Sharon, Pennsylvania. Another sister, Margaret, died at the age of six months.

Helen remained closer to Greenfield, marrying Othel Mossbarger and moving just fourteen miles north to a farm near Washington Court House (a city that holds the distinction among trivia buffs of having the longest name in the United States).

Weighing his alternatives, Roy Konneker accepted a magnanimous offer from Olive to have the children live with her at the family homestead, 768 West Jefferson Street in Greenfield. This also would place them relatively close to the Mossbargers, who had four children. In addition, they would be assured of good educations at one of the state's most unusual schools. Meanwhile, Roy would join his brothers in Detroit as a barber, visiting his children as often as possible and providing support for their care. The decision proved to be insightful.

Winona joined her Aunt and Grandmother Konneker soon after leaving Sunshine Cottage in the summer of 1928. Will arrived the following February 20, his sixth birthday. Winona remembered well the day he arrived. "We still had the Christmas tree up for Will when our father brought him down on the train," she said. "He was a little frightened at starting to live in another new place, but when he went to school, he became accustomed to the town, and got along fine."

In the years that followed, Olive Konneker, a selfless person who worked as a dental hygienist for Dr. Robert Hull, took excellent care of the two children. "I always have thought of her as my mother, even though I called her 'Aunt Olive,' of course," Will said afterward.

Olive was reasonably quiet, never flamboyant, but very personable. Although her job was full time, she never wavered in seeing to the needs of the children, and Grandmother Konneker was always at home. "We had fond memories of our grandmother," Will recalled. "She used to read to us regularly and tell us stories." That influence might have contributed to Winona's excelling in reading and literature.

Things were a little different for Will. Unhealed emotional wounds combined with sudden exposure to an entirely new environment placed him at a disadvantage among other members of his first-grade class. Having missed the first semester, when the students began reading and spelling, he fell so far behind that he still was not caught up by the end of the following school year. His teacher, in fact, wanted him to repeat second grade. It took a visit from his father, who had been a friend of the teacher when they were students together, to convince her otherwise. Driving to Greenfield from Detroit, Roy struck a bargain with his friend that she would advance his son to third grade that fall if he would read a specified number of books during the summer. The promise was kept by both the young student and his teacher, and Will never again experienced a problem with learning. Moreover, any feeling of discouragement that might have carried over from a sadness of the past was overcome with dramatic speed, thanks primarily to the devotion of his Aunt Olive and his sister, Winona, along with the genuine attentiveness of his father in an unusual circumstance. In later life, Will asserted emphatically, "I never felt deprived in any stretch of the imagination."

In retrospect, it is compelling, if not necessarily relevant, to speculate that without his father's negotiation with an understanding elementary school teacher, the course of history probably would have kept Will Konneker from becoming a nuclear physicist.

At the time Will was making up for lost educational opportunities, America was having less success overcoming its deepest concern. The Great Depression, heralded by the stock market crash in October 1929, spread an epidemic of gloom across the nation and eventually around the world. Unemployment affected more than a quarter of the working population. Farms and homes were lost. Despite the American Economic Association's assurance that recovery would be made by 1931, all segments of business, industry, and agriculture continued to decline. This was accelerated by widespread desperation, as serious droughts, windstorms, strikes, and collapsed farm prices added to the growing panic. Total collapse of the nation's economic foundation seemed imminent when desperate measures to prevent runs on banks failed and depositors rushed to salvage their money. Many were too late.

Bankers often suffered more than their unfortunate depositors. On July 2, 1930, the long-established Highland County Bank in Greenfield was forced to close, its prominent founders, the Miller family, losing everything they owned, including their home. Merchants began accepting "script" payments, which actually were promissory notes, in lieu of cash. In some households, problems swelled with the return of jobless family members who had left home for lucrative positions in urban locations during the boom years of the twenties. Nonpayment of taxes diminished municipal and school revenues, forcing teachers and city employees to take salary cuts.

Across the country, unemployed men became hobos, most often referred to as tramps, who rode the rails in or under boxcars, seeking handout food wherever it could be found. Olive Konneker, a devout Christian, could be counted on to feed these hapless wanderers when they debarked temporarily from B & O trains pausing at Greenfield. One such visitor to the Konneker home proved to be an accomplished artist who repaid Olive by painting a nature scene for her. After having it mounted, she placed the picture over the living room mantel, where it remained for many years, a pleasant reminder of a very unpleasant period in history.

The Great Depression unquestionably was economically devastating. Accounts of it are painfully true. But history is recorded through the eyes of adults. To most children of the depression, those years weren't at all depressing. Only those who went terribly hungry realized their families were suffering. The rest, poor as they might have been, didn't particularly worry about a lack of money or material goods. They were happy children enjoying the exuberance of youth. They watched Works Progress Administration (WPA) laborers digging ditches, not realizing or caring why they had such menial jobs. Some thought riding the rails would be great fun. Yet the overall experience of growing up in the Great Depression influenced their financial and social perspectives in later years.

Those were happy days for Will and Winona. Thoughts of the sanitarium were erased from their minds. Will's only displeasure with the depression was losing what he described as his life savings of $4.95 in the bank failure. His father, able to counter the decade's economic despair with enterprising skills and hard work, came often and even took both children to such places as the 1933 Chicago "Century of Progress" World's Fair, a highlight of their young lives.

Like other children, they invented their own games, using old hats, barrel staves, discarded wagon wheels, and other castoffs. Their comfortable two-story wooden frame home, typical of the times, was heated by pot-bellied stoves in the kitchen and dining room, and by small gas heaters upstairs. A large back lot extended past an alley, providing ample room for a substantial garden, where both helped their Aunt Olive grow a large percentage of the family's food. The property also had an abandoned barn, dating back to the horse-and-buggy era, and a separate building that once had been a summer kitchen and smokehouse. The latter became their private playhouse where Will joined his sister in make-believe amusements, usually choreographed by Winona.

Reflecting on the playhouse many years later, Winona said her little brother went along with the fun, letting her tell him where to sit and what to do, "but he refused to join me in having tea, telling me it was too sissified, and insisted that I substitute a neighbor girl to play house. As we got a little older, I think he got tired of me bossing him around and preferred to play shoot-em-up with the boys." Organized recreational activities for children did not exist in the thirties, a situation sometimes defended decades later as more blessing than curse.

Many enjoyable weekends were spent with their Aunt Helen, Uncle Othel, and four first cousins on the Mossbarger farm. The Mossbarger children, Gwendolyn, Virginia, Dick, and Emogene, were family, as well as close friends. Will and Winona took part in regular activities at the farm and always were included in the Mossbarger reunions. Dick, who was two years older than Will, became an expert hunter, bagging enough rabbits and pheasants right on the farm to provide memorable meals for his two cousins from town. In fact, Fayette County, where the farm was located, attracted pheasant hunters from many parts of the Midwest. (All the Konnekers later shared the tragedy of Dick Mossbarger being killed in a farm accident two years after he graduated from high school.)

Summers gave them opportunities to visit their father in Detroit, as well as Grandma and Granddad Standley in Akron. The Standleys remained devoted to their grandchildren, visiting them, taking them to places like St. Louis and Kansas, and buying them presents. Winona and Will always liked to hear stories about their maternal great-grandfather, Richard Hall, who fought in the Civil War. Both children got to know him well before he died at the age of ninety-three.

When Will was eleven years old, Grandpa Standley bought him his first bicycle. Such a gift, special to any boy under any circumstance, had an extra value because Aunt Olive had no automobile. Walking was the necessary mode of Konneker transportation, which was adequate but not always preferable in a small town of three thousand. So the balloon tires of Will's new two-wheeler quickly became almost another set of legs, covering all the streets and alleys of Greenfield countless times. The bicycle advanced from enjoyable to indispensable when he took on daily paper routes for the morning *Columbus Journal,* afternoon *Columbus Dispatch,* and an evening financial publication named *The Pink Edition.* Fortunately, when he completely wore out his first bicycle, he had enough income from paper routes to buy another, which he proceeded to ride until it too collapsed. Reminiscing later on his "cycling years," he smilingly recalled with certainty "riding thousands of miles without leaving the immediate confines of Greenfield."

Meanwhile, Will became intrigued with another possible mode of riding, this one strictly for fun. Retail stores struggling to attract business during the lean years of the depression often announced contests with prizes for continuing patronage. In keeping with that popular merchandising effort, a Greenfield grocery launched a long-range contest beginning in the fall that Will entered junior high school. Patrons were invited to accumulate cards punched with the amount of each purchase made during a two-month period ending just before Christmas. The prize to be given away at that time: a pony.

To a boy with an idle barn in his backyard, such a challenge was irresistible. Competition, of course, would be overwhelming for a small family incapable of affording, or even eating enough food, to win. But not everyone would want a pony! At least that was the assumption of Will and his friend Frederick Speakman, who planned to become Boy Scouts together. Full of confidence, they talked the grocer into supplying them with a bundle of cards, which they signed and distributed to neighbors and friends willing to get them punched when purchasing groceries. In addition, they stood outside the store, requesting the same favor from persons going in. Those not participating on behalf of their own children often complied, returning punched cards to the boys as they left. Periodically, the enterprising pair collected punched cards at homes where they had made original distributions. Few opportunities were overlooked. On a trip from Akron to see their grandchildren, the Standleys were talked into buying a large supply of canned goods, which they may or may not have needed. When the final tally was made, Will and Fred owned a pony.

Will soon learned they had a smart pony, indeed. The day after it was put in the barn, it disappeared by putting its nose under a hook on the door, lifting it up, and walking away. A short search revealed its whereabouts, however. The boys brought it back, rigged a more pony-proof latch, and rode their prized possession regularly in the alley. When proper care in a village setting later became burdensome, Will rode the pony fourteen miles to the Mossbarger farm, where his understanding aunt and uncle permitted him to keep it.

Childhood clues examined in retrospect can appear to reveal basic rationales for what happens later in life. In that context, the pony episode might well represent personal qualities carried on into adulthood. Another could be Will's involvement in Scouting.

From the time he was in grade school, Will had a fervent desire to join a Boy Scout troop sponsored by the First United Methodist Church of Greenfield. Obtaining a Scout handbook at age eleven, he studied intently to be ready the moment he reached the minimum membership age of twelve, and, as planned, he passed Tenderfoot requirements immediately after his next birthday. Never deviating from that established pattern, he moved on through the ranks, at a speed determined only by minimum intervals required for advancement, to become an Eagle Scout. In addition, he earned numerous extra merit badges, to receive the Bronze Palm, presented at a Scout convention in the state capital city of Columbus.

The Methodist church where troop meetings were held was a Greenfield landmark, constructed in 1912 on the foundation of a previous structure destroyed by fire two years earlier. Both Olive Konneker and her mother were staunch members of the church, and the children followed their examples, singing in choirs for a while and taking part in other activities. After taking piano lessons, Winona played for Sunday school children.

Both of Roy Konneker's children enjoyed music, something apparently inherited from their parents. In addition to his mystifying aptitude for playing instruments without instruction, Roy had the rare ability to make high-quality violins, a hobby not easily equated to barbering. When Roy gave one of the violins to his son, Will, still in grade school, dutifully but unsuccessfully tried to get interested in playing it. Later, Roy gave his children a saxophone and a trumpet, inviting them to make their own selections. Typically, both chose the latter. Years later, neither even remembered what became of the rejected sax.

Despite the hardships, Greenfield showed little change during the early years of the depression, but there were major differences in the Konneker household. Grandmother Konneker passed away in early 1934. Aunt Grace and her husband, Harry, who had retired from U.S. Steel, then moved from Sharon to live with Olive and the children. Among the possessions they brought with them was a 1926 Chevrolet, providing the family with its first automobile. After Harry died unexpectedly in the fall of 1934, Will learned to drive, although he was only twelve years old. Two years later, Aunt Grace bought a 1936 Chevrolet, letting her nephew take over what they both referred to as "the old '26 clunker" until it died of engine and transmission failure on a trip from Detroit to Greenfield. Will and his best friend, Johnny Miller, by then were such car buffs that they always were among the first persons to attend automobile shows in the area. Driving often to Chillicothe, they forever after shared two special memories of trips along State Route 28. The car couldn't negotiate a steep hill, even in low gear, so they turned around and went up in reverse. But at another location, a challenging hump in the road made it possible, if approached at exactly the right speed and angle, to become airborne. The two friends liked to compete in seeing who could get all four wheels off the pavement at the same time.

In 1936, the year Will entered high school, Peoples National Bank occupied the stately stone building abandoned by the Highland County Bank six years earlier. But other reminders of the economic plunge remained as the Great Depression persisted stubbornly throughout the nation. Agricultural communities began to wonder whether recovery ever would be attainable. Each sign of recuperation seemed to be countered with a relapse. The Civilian Conservation Corps, launched in 1933, enabled nearly sixty-eight thousand Ohio young men to work in interesting outdoor jobs and send money home, but it ended after three years of operation. Farmers still received less than a dime for a dozen eggs. A bushel of wheat brought less than thirty cents, half of what it had cost to grow. Children in one Ohio farm family went barefoot during warm weather, saving shoes for school months. One of the older high school students cut out "half-soles" from a discarded threshing machine belt and tacked them to the shoes of his siblings. "Store-bought bread is only a nickel a loaf," a housewife said, "but we don't have any nickels." A man who earned a silver dollar dropped it through a crack in his porch while showing it to his wife, and the couple tore down the entire porch to find it. Several persons claimed they had forgotten what a dollar bill looked like. Some farmers who were able to remortgage property through emergency government programs had to use the money for living expenses and lost their farms anyway. Others who managed to keep their land reported the hurt in seeing relatives and friends being evicted. Similar tragedies of the depression tested the resilience of American families, some leaving permanent scars.

Money continued to be a scarce commodity in Greenfield. Yet an overall spirit of optimism prevailed. A community park was in the planning stage, and a new Rand Theater opened downtown.

Sixty-five years later, Will Konneker remembered features of his hometown he particularly enjoyed as a teenager:

> One of the things about a small town like Greenfield was that the children you started with in the first grade were classmates all the way through school. Probably even more so in the depression when people couldn't afford to move, and just held on to what they had. So you developed close relationships. We had the same neighbors all through those years. And one of the greatest assets shared by the whole town—something that still is true—was an extraordinary high school known far and wide for its physical and educational attributes.

Greenfield's McClain High School, indeed, was acclaimed by Ohio's State Board of Education and studied by a host of educators across the Midwest. The story of its founding alone contributed to its mystique, as well as its mission.

Unquestionably the most prominent figure in Greenfield history was a native son, Edward Lee McClain, who founded his own manufacturing company in 1881, at the age of twenty. Having worked for seven years in his father's harness shop, the young man set out to seek his fortune manufacturing sweat pads for horse collars. Incredible as that may seem, McClain reached his goal, not only providing hundreds of jobs for townspeople but also achieving a wealth exceeding even his own idealism. The secret lay in his invention: an open-ended pad that, unlike the solid circular models then on the market, could be slipped quickly and effortlessly under a horse collar and fastened with a special metal hook that he also made. The first products were fabricated in the back room of a bank. Millions followed, as the E. L. McClain Manufacturing Company relocated to progressively larger buildings where hundreds of workers produced 95 percent of the world's collar pads.

After incorporating the company as the American Pad and Textile Company in 1903, McClain created an entire town, Atco, Georgia, encompassing a huge cotton plant that would solve a shortage of material.

It had paved streets, a company store, running water, electricity, a nondenominational church, a private school, and rooms rented to employees for a dollar a month. When new competition loomed in the form of the Automobile Age, McClain diversified into such merchandise as farm clothing, gloves, lifesaving cushions, sleeping bags, and jungle hammocks, and kept on prospering.

Mrs. McClain, the former Lulu Theodosia Johnson, was the daughter of a prominent Cincinnati family. A dedicated patron of various arts and civic organizations, she shared with her husband a love of world travel and learning. Together, they made an unprecedented request that the Greenfield Board of Education permit them to build and equip a modern new public high school that would offer avant-garde facilities and programs. A stunned board accepted.

Land purchased in 1913 for the school campus was just two blocks from the Konneker home. Two years later, the new building, designed by W. B. Ittner, foremost school architect of the time, was completed. Dr. P. P. Claxton, director of the U.S. Department of Education, who attended the dedication with Ohio Gov. Frank B. Willis, pronounced the facility "the biggest single gift ever made by a single individual to the public schools of America." Visitors expressed amazement at what they saw, and continue to do so.

Classrooms and hallways were adorned by 165 busts, murals, and statues installed by Cincinnati art firms in carefully selected locations matching academic areas. Large murals highlighted both ends of the third-floor library, and each classroom featured the reproduction of a prestigious painting. A panel reproduction of *The Quest of the Holy Grail* extended fifteen feet along one hallway.

Covered walkways, white pillars, and beautiful fountains framed a manicured courtyard. One section of the building was crowned with an elegant rooftop garden. State-of-the-art chemistry and physics laboratories were separated by a science lecture room. A modern auditorium had a full pipe organ. Inside a magnificent entranceway were twin marble stairways to be used exclusively by graduates of the school. (That tradition continued through the years; members of each graduation class descended the marble stairs for the first time in a processional walk to baccalaureate ceremonies.)

Eight years after the school opened, the McClain family offered to

complete the campus by constructing an ultramodern vocational building, athletic field, and three custodial cottages, provided the community
would add an elementary school compatible with the high school. After a
lengthy debate, the school board agreed. In addition to metal and wood
shops, a foundry, an agriculture wing, industrial arts drawing rooms, a
three-room business section, an art studio (with a northern exposure), a
home economics room with hand-painted china and silverware, and a cafeteria, the vocational building featured Ohio's first high school natatorium.
Edward McClain explained that with all the boating, fishing, and swimming going on in Paint Creek, every young person in Greenfield should
be taught to swim. The natatorium received widespread acclaim comparable to that of the high school's massive statues.

Perhaps most astounding was an ongoing tradition that protected the
artifacts. Through the years, students have refrained from vandalizing or
even making marks on these treasures. Edward Hope, a 1941 graduate and
former superintendent of McClain High School, offered what he considered his best analysis of this phenomenon that became a source of pride for
students and alumni:

> When we went through high school, we were reminded quite
> often that this great place was donated to the city and we should
> take care of it. I think the tradition was established at the very
> beginning, and something kept it intact. You never saw a mark
> on a wall or a desk. You didn't mar a piece of art. You didn't wear
> hard shoes on the gymnasium floor, or even walk on the grass. It's
> hard to believe, I know, but it is true. The students policed each
> other. The vigilance of teachers and administrators had much to
> do with it, of course, and the custodians had authority to exert
> discipline too. If a custodian saw a potential problem, he would
> move right in on it. I don't believe anyone can explain it com-
> pletely, but is something graduates like to remember.

Although they had known each other as children, a lifelong close
friendship between Ed Hope and Will Konneker really could be traced to
a Pure Oil station near downtown Greenfield. Pumping gas at eighteen
cents a gallon became a weekend vocation for Will after he reached the age
of sixteen. Ed lived next door to the station, so the two became better

acquainted. Such close friendships, along with family, became and re-mained the most important things in Will's life. He greatly missed his sis-ter after she graduated from high school in June of 1937. An honor student at McClain, Winona entered Marygrove College in Detroit, planning for a career in teaching. Fortunately, she was able to return home frequently on weekends and vacations. (After her junior year, she would transfer to Siena Heights University in Adrian, Michigan, where she would receive a bachelor's degree in education in 1942.)

In addition to Johnny Miller and Ed Hope, Will's high school cohorts whose relationships would extend well into the future included George Fox, Dane Iseman, and John Stewart. George was a cousin of both Will and Dane, although the latter two were not related—a situation they found interesting, but too genealogically involved to ponder. All three played in the high school band and in a "swing" combo, performing at parties and a few small dances.

The new sound of swing had surfaced as the jazz of the day, capturing the musical fanaticism of teenagers as it smothered ragtime and other lan-guishing rhythmic allegiances of their parents. Young people hunched over record players and radios listening to big band music on the latest 78 "platters" or frequent live broadcasts. A tiny abandoned house owned by Johnny Miller's parents soon became a private club where he and Will could listen in comfort. Benny Goodman was the "King of Swing" and the favorite of Johnny. Will also liked the "King" but preferred Tommy Dorsey. This difference of opinions led to a coup that lingered as a pleas-ant memory of good times and timing: Johnny concluded their usual de-bate over the two band leaders during the live broadcast of a Benny Goodman performance in Chicago by saying, "Benny Goodman never makes a mistake." At that precise instant, according to Will, the famous clarinetist hit "a real clam; I mean a solid boo boo." It was, he added, "the only time I ever heard him make a mistake, but it came at a very oppor-tune time."

Admitting to the triviality of the incident, Will always was surprised it came to mind at class reunions, which he never failed to attend every five years. But it did illustrate how generations become identified with types of popular music. Most persons forever prefer the style they favored as teenagers. After Penny's Inn, a small frame eatery specializing in hot dogs, hamburgers, and soft drinks, opened next to the Rand Theater in 1937, it became the premiere teen rendezvous when the owner added a dance patio and jukebox. Will and his friends, both boys and girls, were regulars at Penny's when they had time free from school and activities, and they usually came in groups, not on dates. Slight of build, with brown wavy hair, Will was described as "on the quiet side, but certainly fun-loving, and popular." One hundred and eighteen pounds on a wiry five-foot-eight frame kept him from becoming the second Konneker to play varsity football for McClain High School, but he took part in his fair share of sandlot sports, class plays, and the photography club, as well as enough musical endeavors to merit a prediction in the traditional yearbook Class Prophecy that the future would find "Willie Konneker's trumpet wowing audiences on hot numbers."

During his junior year, Will also took accordion lessons, then performed in a trio with his teacher Ruth Hull and classmate Sara Sharp. Bookings during the two years before graduation ranged from church and social gigs to appearances at the Strawberry Festival in nearby Fruitdale and other out-of-town events.

At the same time, however, Will was beginning to decide his future lay in some field of science. Joseph Woodruff, a young chemistry teacher, probably was instrumental in forming this opinion. He had the gift of making difficult concepts interesting and did not hesitate to work beyond the normal boundaries of teaching responsibilities to get students involved in extra activities. With his guidance, Will won a statewide award at the Ohio Science Fair.

In the summer of 1939, before Will's final year at McClain, Aunt Grace succumbed to pleas from her tenacious nephew to visit the New York World's Fair, billed as heralding "The World of Tomorrow." Aunt Grace not only agreed to take Will and his sister, who was on summer break from college, but also let him invite two friends, Robert Kisling and David Duncan. Squeezing into Grace's '36 Chevy, the five traveled six hundred miles to the great metropolis, finding quarters in a rooming house close to Flushing Meadows, where fairgrounds had been built on what once was a marshy wasteland.

Perhaps as an antidote to the depression, the fair defined science and technology as paths to the prosperity America sought. Grace and her wide-eyed entourage marveled at displays and demonstrations. "Technical and scientific things fascinated me the most," Will recalled. "At a General Motors pavilion we rode in little cars while viewing a futuristic highway system with vehicles running over and under complex intersections, and I wondered if such a thing could ever happen." This and other scientific phenomena left strong impressions, but none so immediately evident as an exhibit of hydroponics—the science of growing plants in liquid, rather than soil. Certainly, Will thought, this is something that will become extremely important to the world.

When school opened that fall, he already had read books on hydroponics for one of his science projects. Soon he was growing tomatoes in a barrel, using a screen to keep the plants from submerging in the water. In time, the project was known throughout the school, because the Konneker plants reached a height of twenty feet. "I forgot long ago how many tomatoes I harvested," he said later, "but I'll always remember those vines growing like hell." In following years, he remained fascinated whenever he saw or read something about hydroponics and never quite accepted reasons it didn't become as significant as he anticipated.

The New York experience helped affirm Will's scientific bent, which already had been influenced by Mr. Woodruff and the facilities of McClain High School. David Duncan said the fair motivated him to obtain a degree in electrical engineering (which led to significant work on computers and voice control recognition).

Senior year was a time to further cement lasting friendships and, in Will's opinion, enjoy a small-town atmosphere "where you knew everyone in your school and most of the people in town." The whole town had celebrated in the spring, when Jimmy Hull, son of the dentist for whom Olive Konneker worked, became Greenfield's first graduate to become an all-American basketball player at Ohio State University. A new plant opened by U.S. Shoe Corporation represented an important new step out of the depression. There were many reasons for good cheer and optimism.

Even Nazi Germany's invasion of Poland, followed by a declaration of war by Great Britain and France, was a distant concern. American beliefs that the country could be insulated from such a European catastrophe were bolstered by President Franklin D. Roosevelt's fireside-chat assertion, "This nation will remain a neutral nation." Certainly, high school seniors had little indication of someday being directly involved in a global war. Even though two classmates had joined the navy before graduation, the eighty-three other members of McClain's Class of 1940, like most other seniors across the land, were more interested in preparing for college or other avenues to careers.

By the end of the school year, Dane Iseman and George Fox had decided to attend Ohio University in Athens. That sounded like a good idea to Will, who had thought seriously about attending Duke University until discovering what it would cost, so he agreed to go with his two friends. But first he had one other adventure to pursue. It proved to be even more exhilarating than he anticipated.

Memories of two previous world's fairs brought an overwhelming desire to "make it three, by attending the 1939–40 Golden Gate International Exposition in San Francisco." The unusual circumstance of scheduling overlapping world's fairs in one country had come from a West Coast impatience to celebrate the opening of two historic structures, the San Francisco–Oakland Bay Bridge in 1936 and the Golden Gate Bridge in 1937. The 1940 session at Treasure Island in San Francisco Bay was an abbreviated version of the previous year's event, with a run of only four months. Fortunately, however, that included the summer following Will's graduation.

This time, neither Aunt Grace nor her automobile was available. That posed no problem for Will and a friend, Robert Mosley, who planned to hitchhike, but it required a lot of persuasion with a very cautious Aunt Olive. She finally relented when a Greenfield teacher heading for Kansas offered to drive them that far as a first leg on their journey. The rest is best described in the words of the hitchhikers:

> We had very little trouble getting rides. The president of Gulf Oil picked us up in Texas. Some roughnecks from oil fields, a farmer, and others did the same, and we slept wherever we could find a spot. Once in New Mexico a police chief let us sleep in jail, but at about three o'clock in the morning, they arrested six tough-looking characters and threw them in the cell with us. We graciously let our new cellmates have our cots, and actually, they treated us fine. In Los Angeles, we stayed with a friend, David Duncan, who was working at Fruehauf Trailer Company. Then we went on to San Francisco, where we remained for several days while attending the fair. Taking the northern route home, we had

a rather strange experience with a man who gave us a ride from Lake Tahoe to Reno. He stopped once in the middle of nowhere and tossed out what appeared to be a bunch of ledger books. Later, he let us out and promised to come back after taking care of some business nearby. We were curious about those books, of course, but after waiting for him all day, we accepted a ride from some young Mormons who took us on to Salt Lake City, provided a place to sleep, then drove us the next day to a good spot to resume our hitchhiking. We were gone about a month, and it was the most fun, trying, interesting, educational trips and encounters I ever had. Unfortunately, over the years, hitchhiking became prohibitively dangerous for both motorists and hitchhikers, but it still hurts to have to pass up a hitchhiker when I am driving.

That fall, Robert Mosley enrolled at Ohio State University to study agriculture, and Will entered Ohio University.

Will Konneker never tried to analyze his pervading interest in science, but he agreed his McClain High School experience was an important factor. He and other McClain graduates often met skepticism when talking about their unusual school. John C. Wagner, president of the Class of 1940 who became a prominent Columbus attorney, recalled a speech class in his freshman year at Capital University when he described McClain High School in great (and accurate) detail. When he finished, the professor complimented him on the presentation but cautioned that students were expected to "stick with the facts, without embellishment."

On December 27, 1937, Roy Konneker married Ruth Dunphy, who was born and reared in Detroit.

3

ABRUPT CHANGE OF PLANS

*It is unworthy of a great nation to stand idly by
while small countries of great culture are being
destroyed with a cynical contempt for justice.*
—ALBERT EINSTEIN (1938)

Ohio University, chartered in 1804 as the new state's first institution of higher education, was recovering well from depression doldrums when Will Konneker arrived to begin the 1940–41 academic year as a freshman. Located in the heart of the county-seat city of Athens, the campus spread out modestly from Cutler Hall, a historic centerpiece serving as the principal administration building.

A slight dip in enrollment combined with a reduction in state appropriations following the nation's economic crash a decade earlier had necessitated the lowering of faculty salaries and tabling of classroom building plans. Nevertheless, academic programs had remained reasonably intact, and federal WPA funding had led to the university's first men's housing quadrangle and enlargements of two women's dormitories. Enrollment had rallied gradually to reach an all-time record high of 3,501 in 1940. Fifty-eight percent of the students were men.

America's entry into the escalating European conflict did not yet appear inevitable. Harsh criticism from faculty, students, and townspeople had been leveled at university president

Herman G. James when he insisted on establishing a voluntary Reserve Officers Training Corps in the late thirties. Students joined nationwide antiwar protests. Isolationists, supported by a strong America First Committee, remained a strong force across the country. With the 1940 U.S. presidential elections less than two months away, both major parties, although supporting national defense and aid to Britain, officially opposed participation in foreign wars. Even the Selective Training and Service Act, America's first peacetime conscription of all men between the ages of twenty-one and thirty-five, going into effect that fall, was described as strictly a defensive measure. College students were deferred by law for the academic year, supposedly assuring seniors over twenty-one the chance to graduate.

Early fall national polls indicated that college students felt it more important to stay out of the war than to help England, although a quarter of the men interviewed said they would volunteer if America should enter the conflict.

Freshmen entering universities expected to complete their educations and move into careers on normal timetables. Will Konneker, who planned to major in chemistry, might reasonably have assumed also that a new chemistry building, sidelined during the depression decade but placed again at the top of the priority list in 1939, would be built well in advance of his graduation. At the moment, though, his focus was on more basic issues of room, board, and registration.

Dane Iseman and George Fox were assigned rooms in "Men's Dorm," the recently completed quadrangle on the main campus. Having pondered his resources, Will decided he could not afford at that time to stay with George, the son of a lawyer, and Dane, whose father owned the prosperous Greenfield Grain and Hay Company. He had saved just enough money to pay his first year's expenses if he lived frugally. Winona had just transferred from Marygrove College to Siena Heights University, so financial help from the family was extremely limited, at least for a year. Consequently, he moved into a private home on Franklin Avenue, sharing a room with another friend, senior Bill Gray, who had been a classmate of Winona at McClain High School. A fine arts major, Bill was active in theater, publications, and Pershing Rifles advanced military science studies.

During his first year, Will was careful not to exhaust his minimal funds. After setting up a checking account and paying a semester's tuition of forty dollars, he located a place to eat on the second floor of a building on Court Street, the main business thoroughfare bordering the campus. It wasn't classified as a restaurant, but it offered meal tickets for inexpensive food, served family style. He limited extracurricular activities to membership in ROTC and playing trumpet in its band. Most of the remaining time outside classes was spent in his room studying. Will was invited by his roommate to join Theta Chi, but belonging to a social fraternity did not fit into his budget at that time. Besides, he had reasoned even before going to Athens that concentrating almost entirely on studies during his first year would get him off to a good start and set a pattern for the future. He dated more in his hometown than in Athens, hitchhiking the eighty miles to Greenfield on some weekends and all vacations.

Like all other freshmen, Will was enrolled automatically in the University College for two semesters before entering a major field of study. This procedure had been adopted four years earlier to avoid problems resulting from a mandate requiring all state-supported universities to admit any graduate of an accredited high school in Ohio. President James had justified the structure he had championed by asserting requirements of some schools were so "incredibly low" that "hopelessly unprepared students" could be channeled directly into a degree-granting college. University College provided a buffer where students could make up deficiencies if necessary. Others would be able to move along at a normal pace but without the need to declare a major until the sophomore year. Fortunately, Will's experience at McClain High left him with no deficiency in meeting the university's rigid standards.

Throughout the 1940–41 academic year, Will kept a meticulous accounting of expenses. He made all payments by writing checks, including those to himself when cash was needed, and maintained records of every transaction. In June 1941, at the end of his freshman year, he determined that $400 had covered tuition, room, board, and books, providing a projected guide for his financial needs as a sophomore. (A year later, he was astonished and "quite put off" to discover that the university decided to increase his tuition by charging him out-of-state fees because his father lived in Detroit. His explanation that he had been born and raised in Ohio, and Greenfield remained listed as his home, was not accepted by the administration as being sufficient to overcome evidence that his Aunt Olive was not registered as his legal guardian.)

Having completed his first year of college, Will obtained a summer job at Wright-Patterson Field in Dayton. By staying at home and hitch-hiking the daily one-hundred-mile round-trip commute, he could save enough money for at least his next two semesters at Ohio University. Work as a clerk in the metal department brought his first direct contact with realities of war—supplying materials for military bases around the world. Most memorable was a huge order from Clark Air Base in the Philippines, where a new hangar was to be built. "This will take most of our inventory," Will told the department head. "What should I do?" The reply, as Will remembered it, was that "we couldn't give them as much as they wanted, so we should cut this off and that off, and so on." Clerk Konneker reasoned that such deep cuts meant "they wouldn't get enough to build the damn thing," but he had no choice except to follow instructions. "When the Japanese bombed Clark Field six months later, my thoughts immediately went back to that shortened order," he recalled.

Late that summer, Will, Dane, and George decided to rent an apartment when they returned for their sophomore year at Ohio University. The one they chose was in the second floor of a building next to the Cadillac dealership three blocks from campus and across from a bowling alley. Dane always remembered a humorous encounter with their new landlord:

> While we were talking to the landlord, we could hear the sounds of bowlers and crashing pins coming from the alleys across the street. It was almost as if they were coming from a loud speaker. In the midst of that, the landlord explained all the rules and regulations concerning cooking our own meals and taking care of the place. Finally, he ended by telling us we could stay there as long as we didn't make enough noise to bother patrons of the bowling alley. We all three got a kick out of that, and I stifled the urge to assure him we would try to keep our studying from disturbing them.

The arrangement worked well. Will carried a heavy academic load of more than twenty credit hours, still holding back on his social life, but not with the self-imposed Spartan discipline of his freshman year. Ed Hope, who had been a class behind them at McClain High School and now was a freshman at Ohio State University, came from Columbus on some weekends to visit his three friends. Life at the apartment and on the campus was pleasant, and aspirations for the future were discussed with great optimism. America still seemed destined to play only a supporting role for the war in Europe.

On Sunday, December 7, however, plans of the Greenfield Group, as well as young men across the country, were altered abruptly when Japanese bombers attacked Pearl Harbor Naval Base in Hawaii, erasing any lingering thoughts of isolationism. (The three were to learn afterward that the two McClain classmates who had joined the navy in their senior year died aboard the USS *Arizona,* sunk in the attack.) Student journalists and photographers spending a Sunday morning in the yearbook office remembered the day as "cold and colorless." Some were cramming for examinations, a few organizing senior photographs, several listening to the symphony, "and that," one of them reported, "was how the radio happened to be on." As word spread across campus, the buoyancy of youth turned somber. Students phoned home. Radios became centers of attention, and plans seemed to change in a flash of reality.

The next day, Congress declared war on Japan, and three days later a state of war officially was recognized also with Germany and Italy. On December 19, two months and one day before Will's twentieth birthday, Congress extended military conscription to men between the ages of twenty and forty-four.

When the spring semester opened in January 1942, Will expanded his academic credit hours to twenty-three, hoping to complete as much as possible before entering the armed forces. Manila had just fallen to the Japanese, who were continuing unrelenting invasions through Singapore, Burma, and other strategic supply-line hubs. It was obvious the United States must gird itself for a long war in the Pacific, as well as in European and Mediterranean theaters, where Allied and Axis forces were entangled in a series of offensive and counteroffensive battles.

College enrollments nationwide were being decimated by draft calls and enlistments, with a minimum of student deferments now limited primarily to those majoring in sciences and engineering. Fluctuating service legislation made it impossible to predict one's status from week to week. The only certainty was that World War II had become the most widespread chapter in America's military history. It seemed best for each student on the selective service registry to compare avenues to active duty and choose what seemed most feasible for him.

With that in mind, Will withdrew from ROTC at the end of the semester and joined the army's Enlisted Reserve Corps. The switch posed only one immediate problem. A few pounds short of the minimum weight requirement, although in excellent health, he had to drink a lot of water and stuff himself with bananas just before taking the physical examination. But he made it.

By then the university's National Defense Committee, cooperating with a government speed-up request, had announced a temporary "wartime emergency plan," placing faculty on twelve-month contracts and replacing the traditional two-semester academic year and abbreviated summer sessions with three sixteen-week semesters per calendar year. The summer semester was divided into equal eight-week terms to accommodate students who preferred the former plan, but others choosing to accelerate degree work now could pursue their studies continuously and graduate in three years. For Will, Dane, and George, there was no need for debate. Having accumulated more than the minimum credit hours during their first two years, they could stay through the upcoming summer, winter, and spring trimesters to graduate in 1943, provided Uncle Sam didn't intervene ahead of time. All three opted to do so.

Meanwhile, the trio from Greenfield decided to add another dimension to their social lives during what they considered a combination junior-senior year. At the invitation of Bill Hines, a campus leader and football star from Cincinnati, they attended a Delta Tau Delta summer rush party. In a few days, they became "Delt" pledges and moved into the fraternity house at the southwest corner of the ten-acre main campus.

Will found that what he proudly called his "base of concentrated study" during his first two years brought rewards. Accustomed to good study habits, he was able to blend them easily with building a homecoming float and house decorations, attending parties, enjoying the brotherhood of a fraternity, and making up for his lack of campus dates. He also belonged to the Chemistry Club, Beta Pi honor society, and Alpha Phi Omega, a national coeducational fraternity based on the principals of leadership, friendship, and service.

The Delt fraternity house was a three-story brick colonial structure with a two-story annex, perched near the top of a bridge that crossed the Hocking River. Typical of southeastern Ohio, a series of hills and valleys shaped the contours of Athens County. Beneath the "high ground" of the main campus and most of the city, the Hocking rimmed lowland areas in a circuitous route before heading on toward the Ohio River. From the Delt porch, a person could look downhill across the President Street Bridge at the football stadium, athletic fields, and several small homes that were flooded almost annually during spring rains—a panorama that would change dramatically in future years.

In the distance, across the valley and atop the next ridge, were majestic brick buildings of the state's largest mental health hospital complex. Constructed in the late 1860s and early 1870s, following earlier legislation directing the state to establish facilities for the insane, the Athens Lunatic Asylum arose from farmland purchased by a group of local citizens. Its main building, 853 feet long and 60 feet wide, was constructed with more than 18 million bricks manufactured on the property from clay dug in nearby areas. Staggered wings branching out from a central administrative section provided quarters for male and female patients, who numbered 550 by the end of 1874, the year the building was opened. Through the years, a progression of name changes from asylum to hospital reflected evolving attitudes toward mental health, while the complex grew to include additional brick cottages for patients, expansive farmland, vineyards, orchards, greenhouse, an immense dairy barn, a horse barn, and other outbuildings for hog and poultry operations. Hailed in numerous newspaper and magazine articles as a paragon of mental health treatment, it expanded to some 1,000 acres and 1,800 patients who seemed to benefit greatly from working the fields and gardens and caring for the animals. Production made the center nearly self-sufficient, with enough surplus to provide food-stuffs for the state's penitentiary in Columbus. Ohio University music and theater students entertained patients, and others assisted in their care through a variety of class projects. Both students and members of the community were permitted to share the enjoyment of ponds and picnic areas dotting the attractively landscaped grounds. A favorite self-effacing joke among students became, "The only difference between the two institutions is that residents of the hospital have to show improvement before they get out."

In the other direction from the Delt porch, the setting was ideal for Will and George, both of whom were majoring in chemistry. A science building (later named Morton Hall) where most chemistry classes and laboratory experiments were conducted was a fifteen-second walk from the fraternity house, separated only by a narrow side street. Construction of the seemingly ill-fated new chemistry building had been postponed again, this time, as explained in trustee minutes, "for the duration of the war."

Most campus parties and dances had military or patriotic themes. At one memorable Delt party, "The Selective Service Hop," members and dates had to scurry through an obstacle course, ending with a climb through a window to enter the house. The task was easy for the men. At the request of the army and navy, wrestling coach Thor Olson and physical education instructor Carl Nessley had set up a difficult 1,500-yard obstacle course that was part of a conditioning obligation for all male students.

The fraternity won the all-sports intramural trophy and some social awards, but members pointed out that they also invited members of the faculty to conduct "fireside chats" patterned after those of President Roosevelt and maintained an academic standing above the all-men's average. One of Will's chemistry professors, Frank B. Gullum, who had been on the faculty since 1918, served as adviser to the fraternity chapter.

Students confessing to a degree of bewilderment tended to emphasize fun as an antidote to jagged nerves as they prepared for an unknown future. It was difficult to take seriously the blackouts and air raid alarms in an isolated corner of Appalachia, but they complied. More realistic were the weekly Red Cross sessions where coeds knit for servicemen and made clothes for refugee children. Blood Bank visits to the campus always met quotas. Such activities were blended into campus life, together with Homecoming, J-Prom, Prep Follies, varsity and intramural sports, and the ubiquitous dances. Residents of the men's dormitory complex, where the arrival of V-5 preflight naval students was the only thing keeping one of its major halls from closing, published their own witty newspaper, *The Dorm Dredge*, reporting that social and athletic activities were continuing, despite a steady decrease in numbers.

University President Herman G. James believed students should not sacrifice all normal diversions from academic life but challenged them to remember, "Nothing is comparable to the successful culmination of the war." He exhorted them to make the most of opportunities for mental and physical development and stressed that the policy of the university was shaped to that end.

In addition to his required courses in chemistry, Will enrolled in some specialized studies created to support the war effort. One such course, offered at night, provided instruction in production and use of explosives. Although the primary objective was to help prepare some chemistry students—women and men declared exempt from the draft—for supervisory positions in munitions plants, Will attended simply because he considered it an intriguing area of organic chemistry. He and some of his fraternity brothers also took an elective meteorology course that emphasized the role of weather analysis in combat operations. One of the men in that group eventually became an army meteorologist.

By the spring of 1943, the balance of offensive warfare was shifting toward Allied superiority. General Eisenhower was appointed commander-in-chief of all Allied forces in North Africa on February 14, and in two weeks, German drives there were halted. From that point, British and U.S. troops combined to push their enemies out of the area, taking a quarter of a million prisoners. Plans were being made to invade Sicily, and Russia had at last stopped Germany's seventeen-month siege of Leningrad. Progress was slower in the Pacific, but Americans were winning important air battles and had forced the Japanese to abandon Guadalcanal in February. Conscription of American men into the army, navy, and Marine Corps continued to be stepped up in preparation for all-out offensive thrusts on European and Pacific fronts.

The male exodus from Ohio University extended even to President James, who was granted a leave of absence to serve with the U.S. Department of State in improving cultural relations with Brazil. Having previously served the government in Latin American affairs, he felt he could further serve the nation more directly by leaving the university until July 1, 1943. In his absence, trustees named Dr. Walter S. Gamertsfelder acting president. A professor of philosophy since 1921, Dr. Gamertsfelder had been dean of Arts and Sciences (the college in which Will was enrolled) for the past eight years. Before the end of the semester, ill health forced Dr. James not only to return to the United States but also to resign the university presidency. Dr. Gamertsfelder was selected by the board of trustees to be his successor.

The draft board by that time had called up more than half of Will's fraternity brothers, even though most were in the Enlisted Reserve Corps. Among them was Dane Iseman, who needed only a few hours, all electives, to graduate with a major in business. There was evidence that a mistake had been made, but not enough to postpone his immediate entry into the infantry. Fate, however, was to make amends. Transferred to the Army Air Corps, Dane was sent to Montana State University to become a navigator, and college credits earned there gave him enough to complete his degree from Ohio University. Whereas he had expected to return to Athens after the war, he became the only member of the Class of 1944 to be graduated while he was in Italy.

Will learned that Ed Hope, who had started his second year at Ohio State, entered army service in January, trained in North Carolina, and was assigned to a medical detachment in India, where convoys of trucks were transporting supplies into the country's remote northeastern region, dangerously close to Japanese-controlled Burma. They were hoping to build an access to the Burma Road in order to send materials into China, so heavily loaded army air force transport planes could avoid the danger of "flying the hump" (going over the Himalayas, the world's highest and most foreboding mountain range).

Will and George never discovered how they managed to complete undergraduate studies on campus, other than what they assumed to be the luck of the draw. Neither questioned the responsibility for military service, but each wanted to enter with a degree in his possession. George, in fact, would be able to complete a master's degree in chemistry before going into the navy and serving in the Pacific theater of war as an electronics technician mate aboard an LST.

The priority Will Konneker placed on academics led to graduating cum laude, with a B.S. major in chemistry and minors in mathematics and physics. Yet a precommencement dance at the Athens Country Club on May 14, 1943, could be interpreted perhaps as making his increased social bent no less fateful to his future. More than half a century later, he recalled the details vividly:

> Bill Hines, who had become a good friend by that time, was so popular on campus that he had somehow ended up with more than one date for the upcoming big dance sponsored by the Delts and Theta Chis. One of them was an Ohio State freshman named Ann Lee Hancock who occasionally came down from Columbus to visit her older sister Jane, a classmate of mine. I had met her at a party, but didn't know her well. Bill knew I hadn't asked any-

one to the Country Club affair yet, so he said, "You've seen Jane's sister, and she's very attractive; would you take her to the dance?" I agreed, and had a great time. And I had enough sense to get her phone number in Columbus. That was Friday. Saturday was graduation. I went home on Sunday. On Tuesday I had my second date with Ann Lee in Columbus. And less than two weeks later (June 1), I was inducted into the army at Fort Hayes.

During the next two and a half years, Will would write several letters but receive only three postcards in response from Ann Lee Hancock, who continued working toward a degree in English literature and taking part in Ohio State social activities as a member of Chi Omega sorority.

By fall of 1943, Ohio University's resident enrollment had dropped to 1,306, only 236 of whom were men. Some fraternity houses were turned over to women, and a few were closed. Classes became progressively smaller, some courses were withdrawn, and athletic activities were greatly reduced. Seventeen percent of the faculty members were granted leaves of absence to serve in temporary government positions or the armed forces.

A surprise measure of financial salvation came from the university's selection as one site for a new Army Specialized Training Program. Men's Dorm and a slightly modified women's dormitory, Howard Hall, became housing units for two companies of ASTP men utilizing army-oriented textbooks and course outlines for specialized training in a "basic phase of engineering." These were followed by arrival of a third company made up of seventeen-year-olds who were billeted in Palmer and Sprague Halls. And if there was the trickle of an up-side to the deflation of traditional undergraduate academics, it was in the Extension Division. By 1944, nearly three thousand service men and women were enrolled in Ohio University correspondence courses through the U.S. Armed Forces Institute.

4

CLOAK OF SECRECY

*Carry the battle to them. Don't let them bring
it to you. Put them on the defensive. And
don't ever apologize for anything.*

—HARRY S. TRUMAN

Fort Hayes in Columbus and Fort Benjamin Harrison, a major
Midwest induction center near Indianapolis, were mere way sta-
tions for Pvt. Wilfred Rudolph Konneker. Just a few days after
leaving home in June 1943, he was on a train to Tyler, Texas, and
basic training at Camp Fannin, a new infantry-replacement
training center constructed on a fourteen-thousand-acre wooded
site ten miles northeast of the city. Camp headquarters had only
been activated on May 29, and Will was in one of the first
trainee groups to be stationed there.

Camp Fannin proved to be no ordinary military base. Its mission as a temporary reservation constructed just for World War
II was to train infantry soldiers to replace the killed, wounded,
and recalled troops at the various battle fronts. In addition, it
was to include one of the nation's most expansive internment
compounds for German prisoners of war. American troop capacity exceeded eighteen thousand, with one of the training
programs focused on orientation for Rangers, a recently reacti-
vated army unit preparing foot soldiers for extraordinarily haz-
ardous missions behind enemy lines.

Armed with knives, grenades, and rifles, Ranger trainees were schooled in hand-to-hand skirmishes, patterned after those of British commandos. Most were army regulars, selected from various infantry units as having the potential to achieve top physical fitness and individual ingenuity in combat. Because of the latter qualification, some high-ranking officers at the Pentagon theorized that an even higher standard might be accomplished by assigning selected college-educated men to a special Ranger-style training unit. Will arrived just in time to join nearly five thousand other college-bred privates in the experimental Rangerized regiment.

The next four months were spent marching, drilling, shooting, exercising, crawling under barrages of live ammunition, and throwing live grenades, prodded continuously by battle-seasoned instructors. One trainee, whom Will did not know, was killed by a grenade. Another proved to be former Ohio University student Waldo Devore, who had been inducted before graduation. Will had not known Waldo in college, but the two began a friendship that lasted for many years.

A soldier cannot expect basic training to be easy, and its rigors were not responsible for eventual failure of the Camp Fannin experiment. The problem seemed to center rather on a perhaps understandable, but nevertheless acute, resentment by a cadre of regular army noncommissioned training officers toward the "college boys." Platoon sergeants openly admitted they didn't think college made their underlings "so damn smart," and that they were not "real happy" with the assignment of making them into Rangers, "the toughest bastards going."

If any of the recruits harbored pangs of remorse for feeling unjustifiably oppressed, he could find solace in the outcome. "At completion of basic training, they just lined our group up and declared that the Ranger idea was ended for us," Will said, without a tinge of regret. "Apparently, they simply had decided it was not going to work, and began shipping us all off to new assignments elsewhere."

Will was one of only twelve men from the regiment sent to Michigan State College of Agriculture and Applied Sciences (later Michigan State University) at East Lansing. Even without knowing what was to happen, he considered the train trip from Camp Fannin to be one of the happiest rides of his life. (At the end of the war, Camp Fannin was converted into a separation center for the discharge of soldiers, the prisoner-of-war camp was deactivated, and some of the buildings were moved to a new Tyler

Junior College campus. The abandoned base then was occupied by the East Texas State Tuberculosis Sanatorium.)

The contrast with Camp Fannin indeed was monumental. Instead of barracks, housing at Michigan State was in a fraternity house on temporary lease to the army. Will was particularly pleased to find he was assigned to an Army Specialized Training Program (ASTP) group of one thousand soldiers from across the country, working toward the equivalent of an undergraduate degree in electrical engineering.

The army did maintain a semblance of military discipline. Student soldiers were required to make up their beds army-style for morning inspections and had organized calisthenics. They marched across campus to classes, and they marched back to their quarters, and they marched to the Union Building cafeteria for mess. But that traditional nom de plume for military chow hardly seemed appropriate at a college with highly regarded reputations in agriculture and home economics; Will considered the food some of the best he had tasted anywhere. ASTP classes were taught by university faculty members.

Being just eighty miles from Detroit gave Will an opportunity to spend some weekend leaves with his father. Roy's wife, Ruth, noted that the two men "just seemed to enjoy talking, and each obviously was extremely interested in what the other was doing." There was much to talk about. Roy Konneker's energy and enterprise reached well beyond the popular barbershop he owned and operated in the Motor City. He purchased a second, primarily to eliminate nearby competition, and a third that included a beauty salon. While these remained his principal sources of income over the years, he also bought small homes, both singles and doubles, improving them for rentals and resale. He owned as many as nine at one time, selling only when that seemed more feasible than keeping them for steady rental revenue. The formula he followed emphasized rapid loan paybacks to minimize what he described as "bank use of my interest money." At times, side issues crept into his creative financing; in 1937, he had included the cost of Winona's initial college fees in a mortgage loan he received for a house. And in his spare time, the imaginative barber performed the duties of a notary public, a small contractor, and a real estate salesman. Not to be left in the shadows, Ruth enrolled in a beautician school, got her license, and operated their salon for three years.

When it was announced that Michigan State's ASTP program would be closed in May of 1944, Will, still a private, again assumed he would receive more traditional infantry duties. Instead, he was one of six men in the class sent to West Virginia University in Morgantown.

Founded as a land-grant institution in 1867 near the state's northern border, West Virginia University had become a major research and development center in the forties. When America entered the war, the university pledged its full cooperation, making rapid adjustments to accommodate thousands of young men and women in full-time flight training, ROTC, Cadet Nurse Corps, Army and Navy Medical Officers training, war management, engineering science, radio communications, and ASTP, the latter initiated in 1943.

During the summer months, Will was among a select cadre of 425 ASTP students taking accelerated graduate courses in electrical engineering, prescribed by the army but conforming closely to regular advanced courses of the university. Living in a residence hall and eating at Woman's Hall, he again enjoyed a small measure of college life, except that courses and laboratory sessions were more demanding.

When the program was completed in October, participants were screened for determination of their next assignments. After an intensive interview, Will was selected as one of three students to be sent to Oak Ridge, Tennessee, where top-secret research was being conducted on development of a weapon that could end the war. His records in chemistry and mathematics at Ohio, combined with those in engineering at Michigan State and West Virginia Universities, now yielded an opportunity to enter the mysterious sanctum sanctorum of what had been code-named the Manhattan Project.

Did he have any idea the work at Oak Ridge might involve a bomb? The retrospective answer to that question was evasive: "They interviewed me and I didn't ask such questions." At the very least, however, he suspected they were involved "in something in the area of atomic science," and that was a direction he had contemplated since taking an Ohio University course in atomic physics (the term nuclear physics having not yet been implanted into academic parlance). During the interview, he made certain that particular course was injected into the conversation. Armaments had not even been considered in his early attraction to atomic physics, but his preparations were exactly right for going to Oak Ridge.

The Manhattan Project, sometimes referred to as Project X, was one of history's best-kept secrets. Although thousands of people were involved at various levels of research, development, engineering, and construction, only a relatively few were aware of the overall objective. Dedication to national defense subdued curiosity among participants who were willing to focus on individual tasks without questioning the end product. Yet nearly half a decade had passed since Albert Einstein and a few fellow scientists suggested the idea to President Roosevelt as an imperative response to research they knew was taking place in Germany. A confirmed pacifist, Einstein believed such a weapon could demonstrate its terrible destructive power, thus avoiding its use on an actual target.

The urgent race to beat Germany in developing atomic energy was launched in 1941 with creation of an office to coordinate government-sponsored scientific efforts. Nine months later, scientific teams drawn primarily from leading universities reported to the office that atomic fission was possible through a chain reaction in uranium. As a result, President Roosevelt was told a bomb might become feasible in time to affect the war's outcome. The herculean effort, however, would require a nationwide combination of science, finance, logistics, engineering, and construction nearly beyond comprehension. Moreover, it would have to be carried out rapidly, with all elements working simultaneously and in total secrecy. An undaunted president gave his approval to proceed by establishing a unit within the Army Corps of Engineers to mobilize the finest talent available into what became known simply and obscurely as the Manhattan Engineer District, or MED, headed by Brig. Gen. Leslie R. Groves.

Researchers at universities and some industrial organizations such as Monsanto Chemical Company, some working through contracts with the national Office of Scientific Research and Development, had been searching for peaceful possibilities of atomic energy for several years, hoping to achieve a controlled chain reaction by using U-235, a rare isotope of uranium. The frustrating barrier, however, was that it could be produced only in unfeasibly minuscule quantities. A more promising method would be to somehow utilize a close relative, U-238, a far more abundant form of uranium, but lacking the property of fissioning. Theoretically, this might be done by transmuting it into a highly fissionable new element, plutonium. Under neutron bombardment, plutonium atoms fissioned as well as those of U-235.

The objectives were shifted immediately from developing a new source of power to creating an atomic bomb when MED rallied the country's scientific forces to meet a more pressing challenge. One of the best known among scientific peers called on for leadership roles was another man who was to have a strong influence on the career pattern of Will Konneker.

Dr. Arthur Holly Compton, a professor of physics and dean of physical sciences at the University of Chicago, had received the Nobel Prize in 1927 for fundamental discoveries in properties of scattered X rays (now known as the Compton Effect). Earlier, he had headed the Department of Physics at Washington University in St. Louis, gained international acclaim for studies of cosmic rays, and served as a National Research Fellow in England. In 1941 he was named chairman of a National Academy of Sciences committee to evaluate and report to the government the feasibility of developing an atomic bomb. When plans became action, he was placed in charge of formulating a method of producing fissile plutonium. Setting up a facility masked by the cover name "Metallurgical Laboratory" at the University of Chicago, he had overall direction of experimentation by some three hundred scientists. Most notable, although publicly camouflaged at the time, was achievement of the first successful chain reaction on a squash court beneath the west stands of Stagg Field on December 2, 1942. Enrico Fermi, an Italian physicist and Nobel Prize winner who had immigrated to the United States from Europe in 1939 to escape Nazi persecution of his Jewish wife, headed the team responsible for the landmark triumph. Dr. Compton's coded message to Dr. James Conant, chairman of the National Research Committee, became a classic among war historians: "The Italian navigator [Fermi] has just landed in the new world. The natives are friendly."

In the months ahead, groups in several areas of the country hurried to fulfill key missions. Dr. Compton, who shouldered the additional overall responsibility for the physics of bomb development, already had convinced Dr. Robert J. Oppenheimer to leave his research position at the University of California in Berkeley to direct the group that would produce a bomb. That assignment eventually took him to Los Alamos, near Albuquerque, New Mexico, far inland, dry, warm, and, most important, isolated. A bomb could be assembled there in relative secrecy, provided materials could be supplied from other divisions of the quasi-quixotic venture.

After another exhaustive search, Hanford, Washington, was chosen as the site of a plutonium production plant, the determining factor being plentiful power from a high-voltage line between Grand Coulee Dam and Bonneville. Cells containing various parts involved in the process were surrounded by concrete walls seven feet thick to protect against intense radioactivity.

Plants designed to separate Uranium-235 isotopes from Uranium-238 uranium by electromagnetic and gaseous diffusion processes were located in valleys near the small town of Clinton, Tennessee, twenty miles west of Knoxville. First known as the Clinton Engineering Works, the rapidly emerging complex spanning 59,000 acres of Appalachian farmland and wilderness was renamed Oak Ridge in 1943. A thousand rural families were relocated in a dramatic shuffle that brought in other thousands of construction families to build a self-contained city isolated from the main-stream of American life. Beginning as a muddy prairie town resembling that of an old Western movie, it grew to a city of 75,000, making it the fifth largest in the state. Meanwhile, construction crews and engineers spent most of their days and nights erecting separation plants at an improbable pace. The electromagnetic plant, about five miles from the commercial district of Oak Ridge, went on line in November 1943. With plutonium production still considered an uncertainty by some key scientists and en-gineers, however, a separate thermal diffusion process plant was con-structed in 1944 just as a possible backup. The Tennessee Valley Authority system made hydroelectric power plentiful.

When Private Konneker arrived at Oak Ridge, the town was bustling with activities and growing with new facilities that seemed to appear daily. Fred Argue, a young Stone and Webster engineer on assignment there aptly described the scene: "There were thousands of people from all walks of life, working around the clock, and not knowing more than each specific task . . . not knowing the bottom line. When you saw visitors like Robert Oppenheimer around, you knew something momentous was going to happen. But the secret was held. No one even spoke the word 'ura-nium.'"

Will went to his new quarters fully expecting to become part of a re-search or operations team. But again the army had other plans for him. His orientation focused more on the importance of secrecy than procedures, al-though it was clear he would have something to do with the highly classi-fied project. It was the first time he had attended classes where the syllabus highlighted an admonition to "not say anything." Two weeks later, he was back on a train, this time heading for the University of Chicago.

Knowing that important research was being conducted at the university—though certainly not privy to what was happening behind closed doors of the "Metallurgical Laboratory"—he anticipated a long-running role at last. Instead, it proved to be a one-night stand with a surprise ending. In the morning he was given a leave, told to go home, gather up his civilian clothes, then report, in uniform, to a building in Dayton, Ohio, being sure to follow the tutelage he had received at Oak Ridge. That was it. Dismissed!

Despite the shock effect of such orders, the first thing Will thought of was fitting an army-strengthened body into "civies" he had not worn for a year and a half. But he managed. Refraining from offering explanations at Greenfield was easy. He had no idea what awaited him in Dayton. Seven days later he discovered not only his new assignment but also the rationale behind the unconventional orientation program at Oak Ridge.

The Dayton Project, named in keeping with the evasive terminology of the Manhattan District, exemplified the unparalleled wartime cooperation between government and American industry. It began when General Groves called upon Monsanto Research Corporation, a subsidiary of Monsanto Company, to accept responsibility for the chemistry and metallurgy of radioactive polonium, vital to construction of an atomic bomb. Radium was allowed to decay through a series of processes to polonium, which could be used to produce a source of neutrons that would assure the initiation of a chain reaction. Dr. Charles A. Thomas, director of Monsanto's Central Research Department in Dayton, accepted the assignment on behalf of his company after being sworn to secrecy on its objective.

Although polonium had been discovered in 1898 by Pierre and Marie Curie, no weighable quantity of the pure element had ever been isolated. To do that, Monsanto would have to develop revolutionary scientific techniques, equipment, and instrumentation at its laboratory on Nicholas Road in Dayton. Soon after beginning preliminary work in September 1943, however, it became evident that the polonium operation would require new separate quarters.

Time and material limitations prevented the construction of a new research center, so the company leased and renovated a sixty-four-year-old former theological seminary on the city's west side, more recently used as a normal school, then a board of education warehouse. When the civilian staff expanded to two hundred, additional lab space became essential. Consequently, the Army Corps of Engineers in February 1944 rented the Runnymeade Playhouse in Dayton's fashionable Oakwood east-side section and turned it over to Monsanto. The facility had a corrugated glass roof, a cork-surfaced indoor tennis court, lounges, greenhouses, and an outdoor swimming pool. Both this facility and the former warehouse were surrounded by security fencing, patrolled by armed guards, and lighted twenty-four hours a day, making them somewhat difficult to portray as nondescript civilian enterprises. Yet Monsanto and the army were determined to do so.

The ineffability of Will's recent experiences began to have at least a semblance of logic when he reported for duty with the army's Special Engineer Detachment (SED), assigned to the Dayton Project. A group of servicemen was expected to blend in with the two hundred civilian scientists and laboratory technicians at the two facilities. That explained the civilian clothes. Avoiding public curiosity held a high priority, not only to maintain the supposed separation from any military alliance but also to protect against the built-in panic associated with radioactivity. A sergeant, also in civilian attire, of course, was responsible for locating appropriate housing for SED members and making certain they were aware of problems they would almost certainly face in their strange dual lives. As members of the Monsanto research organization, they were never to wear uniforms in the city of Dayton. Away from the city, however, they were required to wear their uniforms. The two weeks at Oak Ridge supposedly had taught them to deal with such a bizarre situation and stifle any thought of offering explanations.

Will rented a room at a home where the sergeant himself had stayed. The family there had been given enough information to know something unusual was happening when their roomer made unexplained clothing changes from time to time. They were patriotic enough not to ask questions or expect to learn details surrounding the unusual behavior, and they never caused Will to feel uneasy. Outside the home and the laboratory, however, complications were sure to arise, especially with Greenfield only fifty miles away and hometown friends commuting to jobs at Wright-Patterson Airfield and several plants contracted to do work for the war effort.

More than one Greenfield resident saw soldier Konneker on a weekend pass and citizen Konneker on a Dayton street. One friend who was well acquainted with Will and his family approached him at a city bus stop (although Will had spotted the man and tried unsuccessfully to avoid the confrontation) and said with a knowing smile, "You know, soldier, I think I just saw your twin brother in Greenfield last week." Yet he didn't push for a reply. During those years, people didn't expect to know everything that was happening. "I was sure my clothing changes were common knowledge in my hometown, and friends knew something was going on," Will surmised, "but they probably thought I was with army intelligence or some such thing, so they didn't ask."

Incidents on Dayton buses were more bothersome. An example was a woman sitting across the aisle from Will and saying ostensibly to a woman next to her, but loud enough for everyone to hear, "I don't know why some of these young people are so healthy and not in the army; my son is in France."

"I wanted to crawl under the seat, or jump up and explain that I *was* in the army," Will said, "but I resisted the urge to break the sacrosanct rule."

Will's most embarrassing incident was published years later in a government booklet to personalize problems presented to what it called "these young, healthy, apparent civilians in their off-duty hours":

> One of these men [Will Konneker] was stopped by the police who requested his identification. His Class A pass showing special detached duty was not adequate, however, and he was taken to the local jail. Such emergencies were expected and an officer at Wright Field had been designated as a contact man for identification of the SED personnel. As luck would have it, though, he could not be reached that night and the hapless SED man spent the entire night in jail.

The booklet didn't mention that police first checked Will's driver's license, which was long outdated because servicemen were not required to have them renewed during the war. Friends suggested that the name Wilfred Rudolph Konneker might have added to police suspicion. "Nothing could sound more German than that," said one.

Acting like a civilian while living on army pay of forty dollars a month, plus five dollars a day for room, board, and incidentals, became difficult in other ways, too. Will was expected to eat in restaurants and to replace the tight-fitting clothes he had brought from home when necessary. "Whenever I felt like complaining, though, I remembered some colleagues from Michigan State training days who were by then in the regular infantry," he said. "One of my good friends in that group later was killed in the Battle of the Bulge."

Will spent most of his time at the west-side laboratory, where he helped build, repair, maintain, and calibrate instruments to measure radiation. Periodically, he went to the east-side laboratories, which some of the men referred to as the "mansion," to work on and calibrate equipment. Three 24,000-gallon tanks located in what had been a theater area were filled with radioactive radium, allowing it to decay down for extraction of tiny quantities of polonium. This, in turn, would be taken to the west-side lab for final purification, combined between sheets of beryllium to make a strong source of neutrons, and sent to Los Alamos, where it would be transformed into the triggering device for an atomic bomb. Thus, from vast amounts of radium in the holding tanks came micrograms of polonium, smaller than grains of salt, but containing billions of radioactive atoms.

Fermi, Compton, and Oppenheimer visited the group at Dayton from time to time, explaining the overall progress to selected members of the team, including Will, but without saying the word *bomb*. In addition to their anxiety over progress being made by Nazi scientists, who were known by then to be experimenting with heavy water as a moderator for effecting a chain reaction, they were equally concerned with performing an explosion that was only theoretically safe. If the enormous heat from an atom bomb should set off explosions of oceanic hydrogen or atmospheric nitrogen, the chain reaction could end life on the planet. Even as work progressed, Manhattan scientific teams continued their calculations until they agreed such a bomb would not explode the air or the sea.

"Fermi and the others who were the brains behind the project were saying they were 99 percent certain," Will recalled, "but those of us who didn't have their full knowledge, but knew they were concerned, were more apprehensive than they were. I know that's how I felt."

Germany's unconditional surrender on May 9, 1945, ended the fearsome threat of Nazi atomic research. But America's air offensive against

Japanese home islands was just beginning. Soldiers, marines, and sailors were being prepared for an expected late-fall invasion, with casualties projected to far exceed those at the Allied landings on Normandy beaches in June of 1944.

During his hours on the job, which varied greatly according to need, Will worked closely with a somewhat older man, Sergio DeBenetti, who had been a student of Fermi at Columbia University and, like his mentor, had immigrated from Italy. When schedules expanded into shifts so that lab work could continue around the clock in the early summer of 1945, they knew an earth-shaking event was about to take place. Indeed, that cliché proved to be an apt description.

On July 16, an explosion shook the land near Alamogordo, New Mexico. Newspapers described it as "the explosion of a munitions dump, with remarkably light effects." Charles Thomas, who represented the Dayton Project at the scene of the soon-to-be-famous atomic test, described it differently to Dr. Compton, who was not among the witnesses because of a commitment at Oak Ridge.

> The light was many times brighter than the sun. The mountains back of us showed as clear as in daylight. We were stationed ten miles away from the explosion. At the five-mile station two men were knocked over by the blast. The immense ball of flame rapidly going up into the sky was followed by a cloud of dark dust. The hundred-foot steel tower on which the bomb was placed had completely evaporated. The surface sand around it for a thousand feet was melted into glass.

President Harry S. Truman, who was on an inspection visit in Berlin, received the message, "Babies satisfactorily born." After conferring with the Joint Chiefs of Staff, he then agreed to use atomic bombs against Japan if needed to achieve surrender after warnings were issued. Leaflets and radio broadcasts explaining that the United States possessed an atomic bomb, detailing its destructive power, and offering an honorable though unconditional surrender failed to sway the emperor's resolve to continue, leaving President Truman with no alternative to demonstrated proof.

Will Konneker was on leave, visiting his father in Detroit, when the crew of the B-29 *Enola Gay* dropped an 8,900-pound A-bomb named

"Little Boy," destroying nearly two square miles of Hiroshima, Japan, on August 6, 1945. He immediately received a telegram advising him not to talk about his activities or even discuss the bomb, even though newspapers around the world were headlining the story. He was back in Dayton when another B-29 delivered the second bomb at Nagasaki on August 9, leading to the August 14 surrender of the Japanese empire.

That fall, Will was promoted to tech sergeant and scheduled for discharge in early February. World War II was ended, but SED men still were not permitted to reveal details of their work, although they could admit it pertained to the atomic bomb. Rigid security measures and the unusual dress code were continued. So Will was in full uniform when he and a civilian employee of the Dayton Project attended an Ohio State University homecoming football game against the University of Illinois on November 17.

After watching the Buckeyes defeat the Illini 27–2, Will talked his friend into visiting the Chi Omega sorority house to see if Ann Lee Hancock might be there. It had been a long time since he received the last of her three postcards, but he assumed she would still be on campus.

Ann Lee was at the house, as he wished, but she didn't recognize him. "I was in my room when one of my sorority sisters told me there were two young men at the door who wanted to see me," she said. "When I came down the stairs to meet them, I thought the one in uniform looked vaguely familiar, but I had to ask him his name." She did, however, go with him briefly to a local campus hangout, and, although she didn't want to break a date she had already accepted for that evening, she agreed to join him for breakfast the next morning. Persistence prevailed. At breakfast, Will convinced her to join him at a Christmas party Monsanto was giving for its Dayton employees, including the army contingent. That led to more dates in Columbus before Ann Lee received her B.A. degree in December and accepted a position with F. & R. Lazarus and Company in downtown Columbus. By the time Will was ready for his army discharge they were discussing marriage.

When Arthur Compton traveled throughout the world after World War II, he repeatedly was asked the question, "Why did America drop the bomb?" The answer he gave to questioners in Japan summed up the reasoning of his colleagues, as well as himself: "It was our expectation that the shock of such a terrible new weapon would make it possible for the Japanese to resign with honor from a disastrous war. Thus, in spite of the great human damage that it would cause, we hoped and believed that it would result in the net saving of many lives, probably millions of lives, both Japanese and American." Later, another Japanese reporter asked the same question, which Dr. Compton countered by replying, "Would you have preferred that we should have let the war run its normal course without using the bomb?" After a prolonged pause, the reporter said apologetically, "Had it not been for the bomb, the fighting would have continued. We would have kept fighting until the bitter end. I would not, in that case, be here to ask you the question." A deeply religious man, Dr. Compton was disturbed, as were most people, that such a thing was necessary. However, he observed, "Having seen the fighting men suddenly released from the need to invade Japan's main islands returning joyfully to their homes after the two bombs were dropped, I could not say I was sorry."

Asked a similar question, Will answered, "I wish there had been another way to end the war with less loss of lives on both sides, but I don't think there was really an alternative."

5

THE PARTNERSHIP BEGINS

*A good marriage is one that allows for change
and growth in the individuals and in the way
they express their love.*

—PEARL BUCK

Although she was born in Olean, New York, on November 3,
1924, Ann Lee Hancock spent part of her early childhood in
Cincinnati, where she attended kindergarten and the first
three grades of elementary school. The family then returned to
Olean, which Ann Lee always considered her hometown, but
the nature of her father's business necessitated moves to other
locations.

Robert Hancock worked with his father, David, founder
and owner of Union Charcoal and Chemical Company, a wood
chemical plant established in the late 1800s. An abundance of
timber, combined with cheap supplies of natural gas, made a
border area of southwestern New York and northeastern Pennsylvania the center of a flourishing wood chemical industry.
David Hancock's company headquartered in Olean, just ten
miles from the border, was one of several converting logs into
charcoal, methanol, acetate of lime, and other valuable chemicals shipped by rail to all parts of the country. Basically, logs
were heated to extreme temperatures in cylindrical retorts,
driving off the chemicals and turning the remaining wood to

charcoal. Products were distributed through specialized sales companies to steel companies, distillers, and other customers.

As the Hancock business expanded, its company encompassed plants near Jackson, Kentucky; Traverse City, Michigan; and Westline, Pennsylvania, the latter just forty miles southwest of Olean. Another near Memphis, Tennessee, had a grinding operation but purchased the charcoal from other suppliers. Availability of hardwood scraps supplied by lumber mills after timber was cut into workable boards dictated locations, which could be remote. A swinging wooden footbridge across the Kentucky River, for instance, provided the only access other than a railroad trestle to the small Kentucky plant.

Robert Hancock had taken his wife, Ada, and their two daughters to Cincinnati during the formation and initial operation of a distribution center there before returning to the Olean headquarters.

The manufacture of charcoal isn't something a child could be expected to comprehend, so Ann Lee's recollections of her father's work were limited to the excitement of watching men "pull the retort" and walking across the swaying bridge in Kentucky. Such things as retorts and extraction of byproducts obviously were important to the family but nonetheless mystifying to its youngest member.

Grandfather Hancock, whom Ann Lee and her older sister, Jane, always called "Dad," had started the company after completing two terms as sheriff of Allegheny County, New York. While well respected by family, colleagues, and friends as an energetic, highly capable entrepreneur, he was known also for his opinionated, stubborn personality. One of the first persons in Olean to own an automobile, he had drawn unwanted attention one morning when, in an attempt to park the vehicle, he drove right through the plate glass window of a store, all the time shouting, "Whoa, damn you, whoa." In contrast to such impulsive mannerisms, Grandma Hancock was an extremely patient woman, whom the granddaughters remembered for her loving personality and "wonderful cooking."

Fortunately, Robert Hancock's genes seemed to blend his father's competence with his mother's temperament. Tall, and universally described as "easy going," he was an avid sports fan. "I was a cheerleader, so father drove Ann Lee and me and lots of our friends to all the football, baseball, and basketball games," Jane said. "Baseball was his favorite game, but he liked all sports."

Ada Hancock had been reared on a nearby farm where her parents, Frank and Addie Burlingame, still lived. "Mother and Daddy took us there nearly every weekend," Ann Lee said, "and we enjoyed those visits immensely until we got into high school and didn't want to miss anything at home." An intelligent and resolute woman, Ada had become a teacher immediately after graduating from high school, an acceptable and not uncommon occurrence at that time. For that reason, she had not attended college, but was determined that her daughters would do so.

Participating in a variety of activities, Ann Lee took piano lessons, played the clarinet, and sang in the a cappella choir. In 1941, when she was a high school junior, the family moved again, this time to Bradford, Pennsylvania, just across the state line, to live near the Westline plant, which had become the company's most important operation. Bradford's population was less than eight thousand, but it was headquarters for the Manufacturers Charcoal Company, organized and owned by producers, including the Hancocks. This joint venture controlled much of the charcoal sales by matching production capacities of individual members with orders received from customers.

Jane had graduated from high school and entered Ohio University before the family moved, and Ann Lee, likewise, wanted to finish school with her longtime Olean classmates. She liked Bradford, but the desire to return was overwhelming. However, two possible obstacles would need to be overcome. First was getting permission from her parents to essentially spend a school year away from home. Second, she needed the Olean High School principal's assurance of being eligible to take the New York State Regency Examinations even though her official residence would be in Pennsylvania—something that was very important to her. Easily gaining both, she returned for her senior year at Olean, stayed with close friends there, and graduated with the Class of 1942.

When it became time for college, free-spirited Ann Lee was determined to be on her own, rather than follow her sister's footsteps to Ohio University. Her mother, familiar with an outstanding co-op program at the University of Cincinnati, took her daughter to an Admissions Office visitation on that campus, but Ann Lee didn't like the idea of being located in the middle of a metropolitan area. Respecting that opinion, her mother followed a slightly circuitous route home, stopping at colleges and universities along the way, to help her daughter make a decision. By the time they returned to Bradford, Ann Lee had chosen Ohio State. "I was happy, my mother was satisfied, and my father was delighted, because that would give him an excuse to attend a lot of top-notch ball games," she said smilingly, "and that is exactly what he did."

Ohio State University was enough north of the Columbus business district to avoid the appearance of being "in the middle of a metropolitan area." Campus enrollment was one of the three highest in the United States (the others being New York City College and New York University). Yet long walkways across a spacious central campus grassy area known as "The Oval" provided a sense of openness, and views from the stadium and athletic fields across the Olentangy River toward sprawling College of Agriculture fields added a somewhat pastoral perception. Departures of male students had not yet altered the nature of the university, but many of them, like young men elsewhere, were struggling to complete as many academic quarters as possible before entering the armed forces. Within a year, the scenario would change dramatically, as hosts of civilian students exited and those in specialized military programs entered.

Ann Lee, meanwhile, joined Chi Omega Sorority, beginning an active lifelong association as an undergraduate and an alumna. She took part in a variety of campuswide activities, including serving as chair of the Women's Self Government Association sub-committee planning weekend open houses and becoming a finalist in the Miss Ohio State contest.

On February 13, 1946, Tec 3 Sgt. Wilfred Konneker left the army but not his research duties at Dayton. Knowing that he wanted to be married in the spring and return to Ohio University for a master's degree in the fall, Will had accepted a temporary position as a senior research scientist, continuing what he had been doing as a member of the Army Special Engineer Detachment, but this time on a civilian pay scale. He also continued to live in the private home where he and a co-worker, Cameron "Satch" Satterwaite, had two rooms and cooking privileges.

After being discharged officially at Fort Hayes, where he had been inducted two and a half years earlier, he went to Detroit, borrowed an old car his father kept as a second vehicle, and returned to Columbus. From there, he and Ann Lee drove to Bradford for his first meeting with her parents.

With marriage plans set, Will resumed duties with Monsanto, and Ann Lee began her final weeks with Lazarus. A few days before their wedding,

Will flew to Detroit and again borrowed the old car from his father. Unfortunately, this time the main bearing went out before he could get to Dayton, greatly altering plans for their honeymoon, but not the wedding. They were married on March 31 at a Congregational Church in the Columbus suburb of Upper Arlington, with Jane the bridesmaid and "Satch" Satterthwaite serving as best man.

After the ceremony, the newlyweds boarded a train for Cincinnati, beginning a hastily conceived honeymoon trip that proved to be more eventful than expected. A friend supposedly had made a reservation for them at the city's swanky Netherland Plaza Hotel in Carew Tower, but when they arrived, no room was available. Spending the night instead at the Gibson Hotel, they learned from the manager the next morning that it too was "booked solid" for the remainder of the week. However, the manager explained, the Gibson also owned an apartment hotel, which was being renovated, but had one livable unit they could rent. "It was being renovated all right," Ann Lee remembered more than fifty years later. "There were ladders and drop cloths and buckets all over the apartment, and when we woke up the next morning, a whole crew was at work in the living room. We decided that was too much company, so we took the next train to Washington Court House and stayed at the Cherry Hotel, which was okay." Close friends who lived between Washington Court House and Greenfield invited them to their farm for the next night and then drove them to Will's hometown, where they stayed another day with his aunts. Neither even remembered what happened next, but Will suspected he borrowed his Aunt Grace's car to complete their honeymoon trip.

Married life became less venturesome in Dayton, where the couple moved into the two rooms Will had shared previously with his Monsanto colleague, Satterthwaite, who graciously had offered to make the arrangement possible. "Cameron moved out, and I moved in," Ann Lee explained with her typical succinct humor. Four months later, Will and Ann Lee left Dayton, as planned, and moved to Athens, where they would live during the coming year at the home of Herman "Babe" and Julia Curry on Columbia Avenue.

Assessing the background he had acquired as an Ohio undergraduate, through studies at Michigan State and West Virginia, and participation in the Manhattan Project, Will felt certain his future should revolve around some type of nuclear physics. The immediate route toward that goal, however, must lead through a master's program in atomic physics.

Like most universities in 1946, Ohio had not yet expanded its physics and chemistry curricula to the nuclear level, and it was not in a position to have a cyclotron. It did, however, have strong graduate courses, some excellent faculty members, and a relatively new president who was intent on advancing swiftly in areas of research and advanced degrees.

John Calhoun Baker had been inaugurated president on May 11, 1945, when the nation still was living under wartime conditions. A former associate dean of the Harvard School of Business, he was surprised at first to learn that the university had no doctoral programs. Three months later, after the capitulation of Japan, however, he said that situation could be set aside temporarily in preparing for a far more pressing need to meet the undergraduate enrollment surge that would soon appear. Housing and classroom construction became critical, and, for the third time, a chemistry building headed the wish list. In notations he would apply later to a report of the postwar era, Professor Paul Fontaine wrote, "It was actually easier to get the appropriations than the necessary steel, brick, or cement, not to mention the labor." Despite such distractions, however, the president insisted on launching the Ohio University Fund, Inc., that would be used to further research and scholarships, independent of state appropriations, and a system of branch campuses to help assure opportunities for those who could not be accommodated in Athens. Competing for students was not a current issue, as it had been in the past, but probably would return sometime in the future, he explained.

The Konnekers arrived along with thousands of others who bulged enrollment to five thousand. Veterans who attended on the GI Bill of Rights outnumbered total enrollments of previous years. What had been considered capacities for many dormitory rooms were increased by as much as 50 percent. Accommodations for several hundred students were found through a survey of private Athens homes and apartments, organized by a committee of faculty, townspeople, and veterans, and special buses provided transportation for others housed fifteen miles away in the small city of Nelsonville. The Federal Public Housing Authority had allocated twenty-five two-family temporary wooden housing units for married students and their children, to be located on university property near the airport at the eastern edge of Athens. Nevertheless, for a few weeks in the fall, dozens of male students were quartered temporarily in Men's Gymnasium and the Ohio National Guard Armory.

Meanwhile, a fourteen-acre stretch of land known as the University

Gardens, at the foot of a steep hill east of the main campus, was being tiled and filled with dirt, raising it slightly above flood level to accommodate temporary surplus housing units promised by the federal government. When the barracks-type structures began to arrive, one professor noted that "the bulldozers are always just a step ahead of the haulers," but by spring, twenty-three units for 740 male students were in place. President Baker optimistically envisioned this "lower campus" scene as a future dormitory complex, but for the moment, student occupants who trudged across wooden sidewalks covering the muddy ground referred to it affectionately as "Hog Island." Several more prefabricated buildings for married students arrived to supplement those near the airport and were squeezed into a campus parking lot. A large white wooden structure was erected on the central "College Green," noted for its stately elm trees and symmetrical crosswalks, to serve as temporary quarters for the newly organized Office of Veterans' Affairs. Former GIs who had vowed never to stand in another line, queued up outside its door, sometimes for hours, awaiting their turns to fill out forms and receive benefit payments. Other government temporary Quonset huts serving a variety of academic, maintenance, and activity needs, including a student radio station, dotted periodically revised campus maps. Branch campuses already were operating in Portsmouth, Chillicothe, and Zanesville.

The influx of veterans also created a noticeable shift in emphasis from liberal arts to business and science. Consequently, Will was called upon to teach a physics laboratory course while working toward his master's degree in the College of Arts and Sciences, with a highly respected physics professor, Dr. John Edwards, serving as his graduate adviser. He felt fortunate, also, to have as a close friend and unofficial adviser Dr. Donald R. Clippinger, professor of chemistry, author of textbooks, and chairman of the faculty committee on design of the chemistry building that was, at last, positively scheduled for construction beginning in early 1947.

Will and Ann Lee considered graduate school a partnership venture, as they would do in other endeavors throughout their lives. Ann Lee typed her husband's thesis and served as a welcome counsel on grammar and spelling, no easy task considering the topic involved "the design and building of a coincidence circuit using Geiger tubes, and the study of various decay schemes by the coincidence counting technique."

She earned money to supplement their GI bill income by waiting tables at Westfall's Restaurant, a favorite eating house and student hangout near the historic campus gateway. Putting her English literature skills to practical use, she also helped several students, particularly veterans, prepare themes. At times, the degree of assistance was not something she would have cared to discuss with their professors. For her own academic enjoyment, she took a course in psychology.

Will and Ann Lee became good friends of the Curry family, with whom they lived on the sloping avenue across town from the campus. Babe, who had grown up in Athens, received his nickname by being the youngest of three children. He was never referred to as Herman, even on documents. After graduating from Athens High School, he was trained as an apprentice pressman at Union Printing Company. In 1939, he and Julia, who received a degree in education at Ohio University, were married in her hometown of East Palestine, Ohio. Two children, Judy and Richard, were born before Babe was drafted into the army in 1943. He returned in 1945 to resume his career as a pressman. Julia taught at a one-room school and later in the Nelsonville-York system, where she became a principal. (More than half a century later, Julia was to express the continued feeling that both couples had shared a lasting warmth of friendship, kept alive by letters and occasional visits with Will and Ann Lee when they returned to Athens.)

As graduation drew near, Will and Ann Lee faced a pleasant dilemma. Both had decided that Will should continue studies for a doctorate to be fully prepared for his career in nuclear physics. The question in their minds was not whether they should sacrifice the years needed to pursue a Ph.D., but where he should obtain it. His three top choices were Harvard University, Stanford University, and Washington University in St. Louis, all of which offered him teaching fellowships, based on his university and military records. Those universities had the largest numbers of prominent professors who had come out of the Manhattan Project and were most involved in nuclear physics, he explained. Ann Lee favored Stanford, and Will leaned slightly toward Harvard, but neither was adamant, and both saw advantages in all three institutions.

To help in their decision, they requested opinions and perhaps advice from Dr. Clippinger. Many years later, Ann Lee said she remembered "as if it were yesterday" when the three of them sat on a ledge in front of the library discussing alternatives: "After we talked at length, Dr. Clippinger somewhat surprised us by telling Will, 'You are a midwesterner, so I think you might be more comfortable and do better at Washington University in St. Louis than on either coast." It proved to be very good advice.

Having already checked carefully, Will knew that Arthur Compton had left Chicago University to become chancellor at Washington University and that another leading scientist from the Manhattan Project—Arthur Llewelyn Hughes, who had served as assistant director and recruiting officer of the Los Alamos operation—was head of the physics department. Moreover, the university's cyclotron had been chosen to produce plutonium on a microscopic scale for the early experiments, because Compton had considered it better adapted to that purpose than any other in the nation. When Will visited the Washington University campus, he made another pleasant discovery: Sergio DeBenetti, with whom he had worked on the Dayton Project, had joined the faculty.

Will received his M.S. degree in physics and mathematics from Ohio University on August 9, 1947. With little time remaining until the beginning of fall classes at Washington University, he and Ann Lee drove to St. Louis in their Kaiser automobile—a graduation gift from her parents, Robert and Ada Hancock—knowing exactly what they wanted to do, but having no idea of where they would live.

Ohio University's new chemistry building at last was completed and opened in time for the 1948–49 academic year. Dr. Clippinger, whose father was a president of Otterbein College, became director of Graduate Studies in 1951 and dean of Graduate School in 1954. He was also instrumental in developing a Ph.D. program in chemistry, the university's first doctorate, in 1955. Shortly after his death in 1967, the university's largest new building, the Clippinger Graduate Research Laboratory facility, was named in his honor. In the mid-fifties, President Baker's ambitious vista became real when "Hog Island" was transformed into East Green dormitory area, leading to a new era of expansions into the former floodplains. In the early seventies, the Hocking River was rerouted away from the campus to accommodate further development.

6

STRATEGY FOR AN UNCHARTED PASSAGE

*In the United States, boldness of enterprise is
the foremost cause of its rapid progress, its
strength, and its greatness.*
—ALEXIS DE TOCQUEVILLE

Like other U.S. educational institutions, Washington University in 1947 still was rallying its forces of administrators, faculty, alumni, and friends to adjust from wartime shortages to sudden spurts in enrollment and development. Faculty recruitment was progressing well, under an enthusiastic Chancellor Compton, whose prestigious scientific background helped immeasurably in attracting respected educators to this private university near the heart of St. Louis. Students who had returned from the war, the chancellor said, saw clearly "the need for a new vision of world affairs" and "were open to changes that would fit their lives to modern needs" in "this city on the border between North and South." Financial and ideological support from private benefactors was encouraging. The institution's high academic ranking as an independent research university was well established as it approached the centennial of its 1853 founding.

What the university did lack was housing. When Will and Ann Lee arrived at St. Louis, Washington University residential facilities for graduate students were limited to a few prefab units, much like those at Ohio University, and they were occupied to capacity. The best Will could do was add his name to the discouragingly long waiting list. It soon became painfully apparent that the situation was no better in the private sectors of America's eighth largest city. A housing office offered temporary relief by finding rooms the Konnekers could rent, almost on a day-to-day basis, but prospects for a longer-range solution seemed to fade, rather than brighten, with time. To increase the odds, Ann Lee spent every day waiting patiently in the housing office while her husband began his doctoral program.

In addition to his own studies and laboratory research, Will served as a graduate assistant to Arthur Hughes, who taught a basic physics course for a large class of about one hundred undergraduates, in addition to serving as chairman of the department. Will's responsibilities were to make seat assignments and charts, critique work done outside class, serve as monitor during tests, and grade the papers. Making preliminary plans for his dissertation filled the remainder of a busy schedule.

While he was concentrating on academics, Ann Lee was in a somewhat similar, albeit boring, study mode, honing interpersonal relations skills by getting to know the woman in charge of the housing office. "We could hardly help becoming friends when I spent every day there to make sure I would be first in line if something came through," Ann Lee observed. After nearly a week that seemed like a month, the woman beckoned Ann Lee to her desk. "I think I have something that will interest you," she said, in what proved to be an understatement.

That evening the Konnekers drove to an upscale section of old Saint Louis and stopped at a huge stone home that resembled "a national library or some such thing" in Will's mind. Double-checking the address and laughing at the circumstance, they heard the clicking of high heels as they arrived at the door and rang the bell. When it opened, they were greeted by an elegantly attractive woman who ushered them across a marble entryway next to a wide marble stairway and into a cavernous living room. Their hostess, who would become their landlady, was a former silent film actress in her late forties, and the house really *was* modeled after a palace. The click of her spike heels was to become a familiar sound in the months ahead.

An L-shaped two-story apartment forming one corner section of the house contained a kitchen, dining room, living room, two bedrooms, and all furnishings, including fine china, silver, and linens. This was to be their new quarters, available because the current maids, servant, and cook, who had families, all preferred not to "live in." The owners had a son at Princeton, another at a boarding school, and a daughter at home. Because the parents traveled extensively, they needed someone to live in the servants' quarters so their teenage daughter would not be alone. Following a conversation that probably was a disguised interview, the young Konneker couple was offered the apartment, free of charge, for certain responsibilities, most important of which was looking after their daughter when they were away. That solved their housing problem for the remainder of the 1947–48 academic year.

The experiences Will and Ann Lee shared in their unexpected new home life may have equaled those of a university sociology curriculum. They liked both parents, as well as the daughter, whom Ann Lee described as "thirteen going on twenty-one." One of Will's duties was driving her from school to a stable where she rode every Wednesday and taking her there again at 4 A.M. each Sunday, so she could "ride to the hunt." That essentially was the only semblance of servanthood. At Christmastime, Will and Ann Lee were among invited guests at a brunch party for about three hundred of the city's socially elite. Frequently, their landlady would appear at their apartment with pheasant or some other delicacy brought home from a top-rated restaurant her husband owned. The young daughter greatly enjoyed visits by Ann Lee's mother, who would go with her to the stable and pet the horses. There was no display of affection or happiness within the family, however, and the Konnekers agreed, "If that is what it means to have money, we don't want it."

By the end of his first year, Will's research extended to work on the university's cyclotron, which necessitated erratic and unpredictable hours of on-the-job accountability. That circumstance aided not only in furthering his knowledge of nuclear physics but also in his eligibility for a prefab unit when one became available at the semester's close. The luxurious home where he and his wife lived was too far away for viable scheduling, potentially interfering with duties he was expected to perform. As a consequence, he and Ann Lee were moved into the unit, where they lived for the remaining two years of graduate school.

"Living there was another great experience for us both," Will said. "There was a lot of camaraderie, and we had a great time. We didn't have two nickels to rub together, but we had much enjoyment and became close friends with other graduate students and young faculty members."

Ann Lee described the prefab group as "an interesting conglomeration." None of the young couples had much money, but no one worried about such a minor detail. Her observations on prefab vitality undoubtedly offered a wide-brush portrayal of married-student experiences throughout the nation:

> Next door was another young chap majoring in physics. Down the path a ways was Cy Young, an M.D. who went into the service and came back to the medical school as a student, in order to specialize. Cattycornered from the Youngs was Morry Betate, a Burmese Jew, who was a delightful person. His wife was Spanish, and they had a set of twins. Next to them was a young professor of fine arts, whom we all enjoyed as being a real character. Another man was an engineer at the Central Institute for the Deaf. Apartments built across the driveway from the prefab area were occupied by established faculty members and their families. We referred to that as "God's Country." Luxurious in comparison. The wife of a physics professor living there was a concert pianist, and she practiced in front of a window facing our unit. It was just heavenly. We had our own first-class musical entertainment. All of us in the prefabs got to know each other very well, of course. If anybody put together enough money to buy a bottle of gin, we would find a reason to have a party. One of my favorite stories relates to a time we celebrated something special at Cy Young's unit. Will provided the gin and mixed martinis in a large pitcher provided by someone else. We all were sitting around enjoying our drinks and conversations when we heard this sudden sound of splintering wood as Will's chair just totally collapsed. He crashed to the floor with it but didn't spill a drop of his martini. After admiring his deftness, we laughed knowingly at what happened to the chair, because all of us purchased most of our furniture from railroad salvage. Those were some of the best times of our lives.

Ann Lee, who always found pleasure in gardening, told the university's head gardener she could greatly improve the appearance of her unit by planting flowers, if only she had some decent dirt. "What do you need?" he asked. "Oh, I could use a couple of wheelbarrows full of good topsoil," she said. The next morning, she had her topsoil, and soon thereafter her flower garden.

At the beginning of his second year, Will received a research fellowship. This enabled him to drop teaching-assistant obligations and concentrate totally on his own research. Experienced in handling radioactive materials since his army assignment in Dayton, he felt comfortable dealing with the emission of radiation and determining the half-lives of such materials. Discovering what took place in the nucleus of an atom was the basis of studies leading to his dissertation. Hundreds of measurements were required to determine the half-life of a radioactive isotope—the time in which it decays by 50 percent, which can vary from a few milliseconds to a million years from one isotope to another. For example, a radioisotope of iodine has a half-life of eight days, meaning that half of its radioactivity disappears every eight days. Applied for medical uses, this short half-life would be desirable, because the iodine would not remain long in a human body. By contrast, the five-thousand-year half-life of a radioactive carbon isotope has been used for comparison with the ratio of stable carbon to calculate accurately the ages of archeological discoveries.

A substantial amount of Will's laboratory work was creating equipment that would measure radiation—both gamma and beta rays—in terms of energy and half-lives. Putting the resulting data together into theoretical conclusions that had not previously been determined was exciting, particularly when he became senior author of a significant paper, "Analyzation of Positrons," in cooperation with two members of the faculty. "It seemed, and I guess *was* important to present the new data," he said, "but the primary objective of doctoral research is learning how to approach and solve a problem, including developing techniques and measuring devices that are meaningful."

Preparation of Will's particular dissertation was especially challenging at a time when computers were just being introduced as multimillion-dollar marvels that filled complete rooms and had not yet reached universities. A calculator and slide rule served as his computational tools. Ann Lee, who prepared the final copy in its required perfect form on a typewriter, would have been equally appreciative of an earlier introduction of personal computers.

Ann Lee also had a full-time job in the College of Law office. One of her varied assignments there was typing chapters of a book being written by a law professor and mimeographing them for distribution to students. A co-worker, Jean Muetze, better known by the improbable nickname of "Stymie," became one of her closest friends. The two were, in fact, referred to as being almost inseparable through following decades. (Mrs. Muetze's husband, Robert, a retail businessman, became a community developer. Stymie continued working at the law college office, attending classes on a part-time basis until she received a degree from Washington University.)

It was difficult to plan social activities beyond those within the prefab community. Laboratory measurements of materials with extremely short half-lives could be all-consuming, because it was necessary to work steadily during the time they were decaying. Sometimes that could be all night, or over an entire weekend. However, Ann Lee, Will, and their close circle of good friends did learn to know and appreciate certain qualities of both the university and the city.

Some observers through the years had attempted to categorize St. Louis as a southern city, usually because of its 1764 founding as a French fur-trading outpost in a wilderness section of what would become part of the Louisiana Purchase, fifty-seven years before Missouri became a state. However, Confederate sympathies expressed in much of Missouri at the outbreak of the Civil War were not shared by the majority of St. Louis residents. Hamilton Basso, noted novelist and essayist on American history, studied the city's past and interviewed a cross-section of its citizenry in 1949, concluding that it was "definitely middle west." Will Konneker agreed with that assessment.

Positioned on the Mississippi River's west bank, the city was a political rarity in being governmentally separated from the surrounding St. Louis County, headquartered in Clayton. Ninety-one small municipalities, each with its own mayor, police chief, and other officials, were scattered in all directions within the state's largest county.

Referring to the city's traditions, its long-running Municipal Opera and Symphony programs, its museums, historic buildings, a crusading newspaper founded by Joseph Pulitzer, and a reputation as the Gateway to the West, one author anointed it the *grande dame* of the prairies. Indeed, in 1947, a committee started planning for construction of a landmark stainless steel Gateway Arch rising 630 feet above the banks of the Mississippi to emphasize that point.

One of the nation's largest urban parks, containing three golf courses, a zoo, art and history museums, science center and planetarium, open theater, and other attractions, separated the city from the 169-acre main Hilltop Campus of Washington University. Known as Forest Park, it was the site and permanent reminder of a monumental 1904 World's Fair. The university's Medical Campus, east of the park, was within boundaries of the city. (In 1990, the university acquired property in Clayton and converted it into a West Campus for administrative offices, a library, and a conference center.)

Washington University was founded as a private tax-free institute by seventeen St. Louis citizens, with its charter signed by Gov. Sterling Price on February 22, 1853. After debating suggestions for a permanent name, the founders, serving as trustees, voted to honor the nation's first president, whose birthday coincided with the date of their charter. An act by the state legislature made it official in 1857. Although few persons outside the circle of trustees expected the infant university to survive, it managed to grow gradually in its downtown location, nurtured almost entirely by philanthropic support solicited by Trustees Chairman William Greenleaf Eliot, a minister described as being "small in stature and delicate in constitution" but possessing strong "charismatic powers." Dr. Eliot, who later was elected chancellor of the university, was reported to have expressed what became the paramount standards of admission—intellectual qualifications, without regard to politics, athletic prowess, religion, race, or sex—considered avant-garde in the nineteenth century. In fact, in 1869 the university became the first in the United States to admit women as law students.

In 1891, the forty-nine-year-old St. Louis Medical College became a department of the university. Eight years later, another early teaching institution, the Missouri Medical College, became part of a reorganized Washington University School of Medicine. Robert S. Brookings, a multimillionaire woodware manufacturer who retired at age forty-five to devote himself to educational philanthropy, was instrumental in structuring the new medical program that would produce four Nobel Prize winners in the next half-century. As president of the Washington University Corporation, he also helped lead a successful effort to move the university from its noisy, congested downtown quarters to a new campus just west of the city, adjacent to Forest Park. The site was selected and purchased at the turn of the century, but movement was postponed by a financially fortunate leasing arrangement with the Louisiana Purchase Exhibition Company, which was planning the World's Fair.

Construction of the university's centerpiece administrative building (later named Brookings Hall), two classroom buildings, two dormitories, a library, a gymnasium, and an athletic field were financed by large private gifts, some existing funds, and promissory leases by the Exhibition Company. Completed on schedule in 1902, they were used as part of the 1904 fair complex. Then, in 1905, the university's move to its new campus was carried out. The financial procedure was thought to be unique in the annals of higher education.

When Will Konneker was beginning his doctoral work in the fall of 1947, the university's enrollment of 13,462 was almost equally divided between undergraduate and graduate students. He described the physics department as "a great place to be" in a later interview by a writer for a university publication. "It was an exciting place," he said. "We had such outstanding people, and because of Compton and Hughes, everybody from Fermi to Oppenheimer—their personal friends and the best-known people in the field—came for lectures and seminars. We could talk with them, ask them questions. It was an extraordinary time."

Research for his dissertation, "A Survey of Short-Lived Isomeric Nuclei," required the design and fabrication of an extremely high-speed delayed coincidence circuitry employing a newly developed radiation detection unit, known as a scintillation counter. The system was capable of measuring half-lives in the order of 10.3 to 10.8 milliseconds.

As graduation approached, Will and Ann Lee discussed variant prospects for their future. An interview with Westinghouse, the principal builder of reactors, brought the offer of an excellent industrial job at Pittsburgh. Another offer was extended by the National Laboratories at Oak Ridge. Many of his classmates already had decided to teach. Some who had worked at Los Alamos decided to return to the government facility there. All four directions seemed "reasonable and rational" to Will, except for personal apprehensions. "Teaching, however worthy and important, simply did not hold the strong appeal I considered necessary for true dedication," he said. The same was true of large-scale manufacturing, at least not as a beginning. He had no basic problem, philosophical or otherwise, with America having built the atomic bomb, nor his having been involved in the project. "It was a horrible thing, but someone was going to do it, and I was glad we were first," he said. Yet he aspired to "much better things than building more armament," so he eliminated Los Alamos, Oak Ridge, and other government laboratory options.

Having thus rejected all established career paths for a nuclear physicist in 1950, Will began searching for an unconventional direction that might satisfy his ambition. In doing so, he was joined by two other doctoral students, Kennard Morganstern, a St. Louis native and army air forces veteran who received his A.B. and M.S. degrees from Washington University, and Michael Ter-Pogossian, a French citizen who had fought in the underground and earned degrees in that country before coming to the university for his doctorate. Will remembered how they brainstormed ideas and reached a risky but unanimous conclusion:

> We began discussing what we might do, what radioisotopes were all about, how they might be utilized best in the years ahead, and I guess we just talked ourselves into agreeing there must be practical applications for them in medicine, industry, and research. We didn't know what these might be, but we were confident that we could find them. So we decided to start a company, develop a nuclear business, and see what we could do. None of us had any business experience, per se, so it admittedly was a big gamble, but Ann Lee went along with it too. That was quite a decision for her, because we didn't have any kitty build-up and we were starting from scratch. But when we asked Arthur Compton for his opinion, he was very encouraging. In view of his tremendous background and knowledge, that further increased our confidence.

The chancellor even suggested that the U.S. government might be willing to subsidize them for specified federal research, but the young men were adamant in wanting to begin strictly as a private commercial enterprise. That determination in no way diminished the moral support of Dr. Compton, nor of Professor Hughes, who warned that the first few years might prove to be lean but believed they would succeed.

Industrial use of radioactivity offered some logical applications of the things they had been researching. Medicine, however, was even more promising. Radioisotopes already were being introduced in university hospitals, on a very limited scale, mostly to test thyroid functions and to treat leukemia.

Although a classmate, Ken Morganstern was six months behind Will and Michael because he had not finished his dissertation research project. That meant he would work part time with the proposed company until completing his degree requirements. Then, before start-up, Michael accepted a full-time position with the university's Barnes Hospital, a teaching unit of the School of Medicine that decided it needed a physicist to develop nuclear medical programs. He wanted to work part time with the proposed new company, but Will was convinced conflicts with such an arrangement would be inevitable. Michael reluctantly withdrew, leaving Will the only full-time member of the now two-man team.

Even before June commencement, soon-to-be Dr. Konneker and his partner formed Nuclear Research and Development, Inc., and moved what little laboratory equipment they had into a one-story, one-thousand-square-foot storefront at 1094 Sutter Avenue in University City, within walking distance of the campus. Their commercial neighbor was a bar, and their headquarters had storefront windows with no identifying sign. Walk-in business could hardly be expected, and the general public at that time still recoiled at the sight or sound of the word *nuclear*. It had, in fact, taken strong persuasion to convince their landlord that his building was not in danger of being blown up. When word did circulate that something technical was happening inside the building, a few persons brought radios in for repairs.

Ann Lee became the company's first secretary-treasurer, with what she described as "janitorial side duties." Reflecting on her fiscal responsibilities, she said, "They were quite uncomplicated; if we needed the money one month, we got it, and if the company needed it, the company got it." She believed Will was motivated partly by a strong feeling of independence, and she was undisturbed by prospects of an initial struggle, explaining, "We had lived on next to nothing for so many years, a few more didn't make that much difference."

Will received his Doctor of Philosophy degree in nuclear physics at the June 6, 1950, commencement of Washington University in St. Louis.

One of the largest crowds in the history of the university, including his sister, his father, and his father's wife, filled the Field House for graduation ceremonies featuring a televised major address by Elder Statesman Bernard M. Baruch. In addition, two thousand extra seats were placed on the lawn outside the Field House, where the proceedings were heard over a public address system. Showing what a reporter described as "genial good humor, enthusiasm, and interest in the commencement exercises," and knowing that he was about to receive an honorary doctor of laws degree, octogenarian Baruch began his talk by addressing "fellow graduates and your families."

The noted speaker, who had been an adviser to every U.S. president from Woodrow Wilson to Dwight Eisenhower and had been appointed by Harry Truman to the United Nations Atomic Energy Commission, came to the campus from his New York home at the invitation of Chancellor Compton. Speaking from experience of rising from an office boy in a brokerage house to a self-made millionaire investor with his own Wall Street firm, and subsequent important national economic leadership positions during both World Wars and the Great Depression, he emphasized the need to "wage peace" while concentrating also on being fully armed against the threat of aggression. At a time when Senate committees were attracting nationwide attention with investigations of alleged subversive activities, Baruch supported a "search for treason" but warned that it should not mean "seeing a Communist under every bed." The "first and foremost of our national policies," he said, "is to establish and maintain world peace."

Many of the 2,201 men and women receiving degrees from Dr. Compton that day believed Baruch's thoughts extended beyond what they had anticipated to be a "typical going-out-into-the-world" commencement talk, to offer a realistic prediction of what they were likely to encounter while carving careers in the last half of the century. Those who might have thought they were hearing the words of a man whose own career was essentially completed were to be surprised. Although his memoirs were published near the end of the decade, Bernard Baruch's opinions continued to be highly regarded until his death in 1965, at the age of ninety-five.

No longer eligible for a prefab unit, Will and Ann Lee moved into an apartment on Clemens Avenue, about halfway between the university and the new company quarters. Bachelor Morganstern lived with his parents at nearby Park Edge Lane while finishing his dissertation studies.

A report written by Will defined the original purpose of the corporation: "To offer technical services to both the medical profession and industry in the new field of nuclear technology . . . in the form of consultation and training, as well as in the performance of research projects for clients." In anticipation of continuing growth, it added that the charter provided for an even wider scope of operations in the future.

Self-confidence being the best form of security, the Konnekers and their business partner felt comfortable with their chances for success. They had their corporate charter, their laboratory, their research backgrounds, youth, exuberance, initiative, and a strategic plan. All they really lacked were customers.

Will Konneker regretted Michael Ter-Pogossian's disappointment when it became necessary to decline his proposal to work part time with the new company while employed at Barnes Hospital, and he was most pleased when their friendship resumed a few years later. Will became one of Michael's strongest backers when the young French physicist developed a diagnostic method of pinpointing tumors, known as positron emission tomography, and felt his friend should have received a Nobel Prize. Dr. Ter-Pogossian's findings in future years would lead to what the Academy of Science of St. Louis described as an explosion of new knowledge about heart attacks, cancer, and how the brain works. In 1995, he was presented the academy's highest award for his lifetime contributions to science and humanity.

7

PIONEERS OF NUCLEAR MEDICINE

*Do not follow where the path may lead. Go in-
stead where there is no path, and leave a trail.*
—ANONYMOUS

At the age of twenty-eight, Will Konneker and his twenty-
five-year-old partner, Ken Morganstern, targeted Jewish Hospital, recognized as one of the best in the Midwest, as a
possible first client for their business enterprise. The hospital's
radiologist and pathologist were interested in starting a nuclear medicine program, but the board of directors remained
unconvinced of its feasibility. Such an endeavor would have
to be licensed by the Atomic Energy Commission, which demanded a rigid set of rules, including expensive equipment
and supervision by a qualified physicist, either as a staff member or a consultant. No private hospital in St. Louis, and few
in the country, for that matter, other than some affiliated with
universities, had publicly recognized such a need. The board
was, however, willing to hear a presentation from the Nuclear
Research and Development owners.

The two young physicists outlined advantages of being in
the forefront of such an important innovation as nuclear medicine, and how they would provide consulting and training
services for physicians and technicians, while helping them

gain the all-important approval and cooperation of the AEC. They explained that such radioisotopes as those of iodine and phosphorous had been shown, through use in university hospitals, to be effective in measuring and relieving hyperthyroid conditions, locating tumors, and treating certain cancers, such as leukemia. After several sessions, they were given the assignment—with a consulting fee of one hundred dollars a month.

Jewish Hospital proved to be their sole source of income for several months, primarily because Will was there so often he didn't have much time left for attracting new clients. Yet it gave them the impetus they needed.

Will had not studied life sciences in college. His concentration had been on pure sciences—chemistry, physics, engineering, and related subjects—so he made an agreement with the hospital's pathologist to instruct him in handling radioactive materials and assist in his research while he, in turn, taught Will rudiments of physiology and biology. The arrangement worked so well, Will felt that he was a combination teacher and resident at Jewish Hospital for the remainder of 1950. In that time, he and Ken (who still was working part time) installed, calibrated, and repaired special equipment. They scrutinized materials, sinks, and floors for possible contamination and made "film badges" to monitor radiation received by all persons who handled radioactive materials.

At that point in nuclear medicine, utilizing a special isotope of iodine to measure thyroid function represented the major test being performed. The only source of this material was the Atomic Energy Commission at Oak Ridge, Tennessee. Jewish Hospital did not want to set up an in-house "hot lab" to handle large quantities of radioisotopes, so Nuclear Research and Development, Inc., established such a facility at its own Sutter Street location. Material was ordered from Oak Ridge by the hospital but shipped directly to NRD laboratories, where it was processed and broken down into individual doses required by the doctors.

Bolstered by attainments at Jewish Hospital, the Konneker-Morganstern combine signed a similar contract with St. Johns Hospital, the City Hospital, County Hospital, and others in the St. Louis area, moving as rapidly as the new clients could obtain necessary licensing. Essentially, they set up clinical isotope laboratories (later to become nuclear medicine departments) for client hospitals, ordering or building equipment, training physicians and technicians, consulting on regular schedules—at least once a month—and doing whatever else was necessary to provide a complete service package. But dividing radioactive materials and dispensing individual units remained their exclusive responsibility. Hospital staffs could learn procedures but had neither the qualifications nor the desire to attempt that fundamental function of nuclear medicine.

Will and Ken had no problem ordering and breaking down the materials, but having each individual hospital order its own material to be shipped to NRD labs was inconvenient, as well as unnecessarily expensive. It seemed far more logical, the men thought, for their company to order a single large supply of their own, process it into individual doses, and sell those as needed to hospitals. Clients agreed unanimously, realizing such an arrangement would eliminate an unproductive intermediate bit of red tape. There was some apprehension, however, that the Atomic Energy Commission would balk at the idea of doling out such large quantities of radioactive materials to a youthful pair of relatively new businessmen, despite their credentials.

A trip to Oak Ridge erased that doubt. Carefully preparing a convincing presentation, as they had done for the hospital board, the two gained approval for their proposal. Dr. S. Allen Lough, chief of AEC isotopes distribution, reportedly said that, among other things, he was dazzled to be confronted by research scientists who were not seeking government grants. The plan was put into action immediately. Supplies were purchased directly, split into individual doses, and sold, ready to use, to the hospitals.

Subsequently, the two young owners made periodic trips to Oak Ridge laboratories, returning with cargoes of radioactive cobalt weighing fractions of ounces but enclosed in an eight-hundred-pound safe on the back of a small enclosed delivery truck bearing large bright warning signs. Neither recalled having the slightest hint of a traffic problem. Motorists gave them wide berth when they spotted the word *radioactive*. The fact that the material would be used to save patients' lives was an irony in comparison with public reaction to that fearsome term. When supplies began to be delivered in a more economic manner—five-pound concrete and lead containers sealed in larger steel shells and sent air express—a similar response from handlers was elicited by the AEC-required labeling, "Class D Poison—Radioactive Material—Immediate Delivery. No person shall remain within three feet of this container unnecessarily."

Dr. Konneker often demonstrated with a detector that a radium-dial wristwatch emitted more radiation than his packages. That satisfied delivery companies and most handlers, but Konneker never disagreed with the importance of being extremely careful in handling radioactive materials, inside and outside his laboratories, the hospitals they served, and en route.

There were times when widespread misconceptions spawning the false aura of "nuclear energy" proved advantageous. On one occasion in the company's dawning years, Will went to a St. Louis bank, seeking a much-needed loan of $2,000, a sizable amount at that time for a relatively unknown entrepreneur. Prepared to offer an explanation and appropriate credentials, he was amazed to discover that none was needed. "Just sign here," the bank president said, without asking even one question. Many years later, when the two had become friends, Will mentioned the incident and his surprise at the ease of receiving a loan. "I remember it well," the banker replied with a smile. "I knew you were in nuclear something or other, and I just supposed I shouldn't ask too many questions."

Personal, as well as business, financing was challenging in those formative years of the company. Nevertheless, the Konnekers decided it was time to leave their apartment and begin building equity by purchasing a small house in Rock Hill, a suburban municipality west of the city. Recalling that chapter in their married life later drew a hearty laugh from Ann Lee. "Dick Rosenthal, an insurance agent friend, examined our finances at the time," she said. "Not only did he conclude that we couldn't afford insurance, he expressed great wonder that we were even keeping solvent. But we managed to buy the house, and pretty soon things started going well for us."

Rosenthal, who represented Mutual of New York, stayed in touch with the Konnekers, although it was literally true that he had closed the ledger, told his friends, "You can't afford insurance," and walked out the door. The incident had no effect on their friendship, which continued to grow, and several years later Will did purchase a policy. This triggered a chain of ideas by Dick Rosenthal, MONY, and its advertising agency, based on the salesman's intrigue with the NRD lab and things that were happening there. Why not parlay Will's story and an appropriate photograph into an advertisement for magazines? "The company would like to use your experience as an example of why and how people buy life insurance," Rosenthal said. Encountering no opposition from Will, the ad agency promptly dispatched a team of New York photographers to St. Louis, where they shot a wide array of scenes, not only at the lab but also at the Konneker home. Will, who signed away one-time circulation rights, received no monetary compensation, but he was given an impressive portfolio of company and family photos. The advertisement featured a large picture showing "Dr. Wilfred Konneker, St. Louis nuclear physicist specializing in radioactive pharmaceuticals," at work in his lab. Beneath it appeared the headline, "I need lab equipment . . . not life insurance!" followed by a subhead, "That's what I said . . . until a MONY man impressed me with a scientific approach." An explanation in the body below provided a reasonably accurate account of what had taken place, albeit in the copy-writing dialect of advertising. Full-page versions received prominent placements in some of the country's top-rated news and feature magazines. Six months later they appeared again, even though Will had not given permission for the second round. Despite urging by acquaintances and admissions by the advertiser, however, he dismissed any thought of a lawsuit. That kind of action simply wasn't his style.

Neighborhood camaraderie blossomed at Rock Hill. Attorney Robert Allen lived just four doors away, and Marshall Cleland, a Nuclear Research and Development scientist who had been a classmate of Will at Washington University, lived on a nearby corner. The three couples and others socialized frequently and formed an investment club, Capital Twelve Ltd., which met regularly in members' homes. "We got to know each other very well," Allen said, "and although I did not represent Will's company at the time, I did several things for him, and for Ann Lee, in future years." Cleland, after receiving his Ph.D., worked for the Naval Research Laboratories in Washington before Will enticed him to join his company.

While remaining true to its name, Nuclear Research and Development also became the first firm to supply premeasured, precalibrated, single-dose vials, or capsules, of radiolabeled drugs for use by the medical profession without further handling. As such, it was recognized as the world's first radiopharmaceutical company. Later, somewhat to the chagrin of the scientific-minded owners, that title would be popularized by newspapers and magazines as the world's first atomic drugstore. From a layman's point of view, perhaps the media interpretation should not be faulted.

Neither could reporters be blamed entirely for having difficulty understanding details of the business. For one thing, comprehension of isotopes alone could not be conveyed in general terms without explaining how atoms of an element, ordinarily containing equal numbers of positively charged protons and neutrally charged neutrons in their nuclei, could be altered in reactors or cyclotrons to create imbalances that changed them into radioactive isotopes. It was no less puzzling to visualize colorless, tasteless, odorless merchandise that had essentially no weight, could not be seen, and was shipped in tiny bottles of water encased in lead containers. Units were measured in curies (named after Madam Curie) by the amount of emitted radiation, rather than weight, and calibration of doses had to be based upon both the half-life of each type of isotope and the scheduled time of delivery. If an order for ten units was to be delivered the following day, it would have to be calibrated at a much higher figure to account for half-life decay. Yet, enough doses to supply twenty hospitals might be contained in two cubic centimeters of liquid. One interviewer remarked that while a meaningful understanding of the process eluded his nonscientific aptitudes, the total subject was nonetheless fascinating just in its complexity.

Work in the laboratory was done with tongs and other remote-handling devices, behind lead barriers, using mirrors for vision. Asphalt tiling was used as floor covering so pieces could be taken up and replaced immediately if any radioactive material should be dropped. Gloves, cups, and napkins were metered regularly for contamination, disposed of in special vaults, where they were allowed to decay until no radiation could be measured, then put into regular trash bins.

A newspaper reporter speculated that the company was "on the ground floor of nuclear medicine," but Will Konneker responded modestly, "No, we are in the subbasement." While the business was expanding, Will applied some of the research he had done as a graduate student developing new instruments and circuits to improve the sensitivity of measuring radioactivity. Geiger counters being used as detectors seemed inadequate for new isotope programs in nuclear medicine, where it was critical to use the least possible amount of radioactive material. Much more sensitive "scintillation counters," which resulted from research at Washington University, could not at that time be purchased in the commercial marketplace. By reflecting on his earlier studies, and using the new photoelectric tubes developed by the government during the war, however, Will was able to design and build an electronic instrument that was ten times more sensitive in the detection of gamma radiation than a Geiger counter. This meant a patient would need to receive just one-tenth the previously administered tracer dosage of radioactive iodine—dubbed an "atomic cocktail"—to obtain the desired measurements, increasing safety by a factor of ten. That put the company immediately into a second business, instrument manufacturing. Its new products represented the world's first commercially available scintillation counters, which later became the backbone of the nuclear medicine industry.

Ken Morganstern had received his Ph.D. in 1951 and joined Will in full-time work, but expansion into a new field, along with continued growth in radiopharmaceuticals, necessitated hiring more assistants. Foremost among them was Karl Wolfe, who held a master's degree in nuclear physics and was working on the cyclotron at Washington University. In addition to those qualifications, he had learned tool and die making and machine design in a shop owned by his family.

It was Karl who designed the final package and set up the small manufacturing operations to help improve subsequent models of the scintillation counter. He designed a mobile unit with a flexible arm holding the scintillation detector and auxiliary circuitry, and a lower cabinet holding a recorder, so that the entire unit, dubbed the "Scanograph," could be wheeled right up to a bedridden patient. Jewish Hospital received distinction within the profession for this and other innovations by Nuclear Research and Development, further enhancing NRD's image and therefore its growth.

During the following two years, the corporation formed a separate division, the NRD Instrument Company, headed by Wolfe, to develop and market a complete line of radiation detection equipment designed not only for consulting clients but also for the general medical and scientific markets. Robert Buntaine, formerly with Nuclear Chicago, a competing instrument company, joined NRD as sales and marketing manager. However, consulting remained the keystone of the enterprise as the list of clients grew and spread across the country more rapidly than either of the founders had imagined.

Offices and laboratories were moved around the corner from Sutter to Wellston Avenue, where another leased building offered ten times more space, including room for an expanded machine shop. Most machinery used to manufacture the electronic equipment remained at that location when Konneker and Morganstern relocated their labs and offices once again, this time to a larger leased facility at 9842 Manchester Road, a few blocks from Will's Rock Hill home. The largest of four main laboratory areas was devoted to producing one of the nation's first and most complete lines of radiopharmaceuticals for general, veterans, and university research hospitals and private clinics throughout the United States and in several foreign countries. New products were developed for industry and government, as well as the medical profession, in a separate chemical research laboratory. In the third counting area, considered one of the best in the Midwest, research associates detected and measured radioactivity sources in a multitude of physical forms—solid, liquid, and gaseous—then analyzed them for alpha, beta, or gamma radiation. A well-equipped and staffed physics lab for research and development of special projects occupied the fourth section. A former ranch-style home attached to the back of the building, occupied previously by the owner of a real estate agency, was converted to office and conference quarters.

Concerns with possible perils still seemed to attract media attention. In a December 1953 *Coronet* magazine article about the company, writer Peter Wyden described the driving of Ralph E. Nuelle, a research physicist who routinely made deliveries to St. Louis hospitals:

> Every Tuesday morning, Ralph Nuelle tucks a handful of little bottles into the watertight plastic compartments of a lead-lined tool box bearing the red three-leaved clover insignia that means "Danger! Radioactivity." He locks the box, wedges it into the back of an otherwise empty truck, and drives off to make his rounds of the hospitals. Nuelle's driving is a safety-expert's dream. He turns corners slowly and smoothly, never making a sudden stop. He gives everybody the right of way. When he unloads his box at a hospital, he holds it firmly and steps gingerly, making sure that he will not drop his load.

Judging capabilities of staff members, including the two owners, by any given assignment would have been vastly misleading. Hubris did not fit into the company profile. Typical of most employees, Ralph Nuelle, the Tuesday deliveryman, had a versatile scientific background worthy of his primary research responsibilities. A graduate of the University of Missouri, he had five years' experience as the cyclotron engineer for Washington University's physics department and specialized in several related fields, including calibration and production of radioisotopes.

More than one hundred hospitals had full-package agreements with the company in 1953, and electronic equipment sales were soaring. After studying trends on the eastern seaboard, with its high potential for growth, Ken Morganstern moved to New York City, where he established a branch laboratory in the Astoria section of Queens, near midtown Manhattan. To overcome a title conflict in registering to do business in New York, Nuclear and Research Development changed its corporate name to Nuclear Consultants, Inc. (NCI).

Will and employees at St. Louis continued to prepare radiopharmaceutical materials and equipment for shipment to the New York lab for distribution to eastern clients. The products were in particular demand at hospitals that wanted to emphasize their ability to keep abreast of all new developments, so the company adopted that concept as its advertising theme. Some hospitals received advice and assistance from university researchers, but few of those scientists could offer the concentrated effort of a commercial organization. Eventually, two major pharmaceutical corporations, Abbott Laboratories and Squibb, became competitors, but NCI doggedly held its lead. Working capital at that point in the company's history became the only limiting factor for sustained growth.

Such a string of successes nationwide was destined to draw attention from large investors. One such group, Telautograph, owned a multimillion-dollar corporate shell on the New York Stock Exchange, a residue from Reo Motor Company's sale of its Michigan plant and facilities to a competitor, White Motors. Familiar with that situation and mindful of NCI's interest in fresh capital, Morganstern utilized personal connections to negotiate a merger into the Reo Motor shell. On October 7, 1955, this evolved into the formation of a new corporate entity named Nuclear Corporation of America (NCA). Through a favorable stock and cash arrangement NCI became a wholly owned subsidiary of NCA, with Will continuing his responsibilities as vice president in charge of St. Louis operations at the Manchester Road headquarters and Ken remaining in New York. The NCA securities received by the two men through the merger were traded on the American Stock Exchange.

Nuclear Corporation of America decided to move the NRD Instrument Company to New Jersey to be housed with another group, NCA Electronics. Rather than move east, however, Karl Wolfe, along with others who had been working at the Wellston Avenue facility, left the company to start their own business, Designs for Tomorrow, which produced prototypes of mechanical equipment.

Meanwhile, Will joined Marshall Cleland and Johnathan Townsend, a Washington University professor, in founding a start-up St. Louis corporation they named Telray. Cleland conceived the idea of developing a million-volt X-ray machine in a totally new way (using vacuum tubes) and expressed a desire to expand it into a separate new company. He proposed leaving NCI to work full time on the project, with Konneker handling the financing and serving as a corporate adviser, in addition to being part owner. In consummating an agreement to launch Telray, Will Konneker took the first of what would become several entrepreneurial steps outside the confines of his dominant business. He and Townsend essentially became passive members of the executive group, with Cleland managing day-to-day activities at a small laboratory in suburban Kirkwood. Bob Allen served as legal representative for the fledgling company.

Nuclear Corporation of America intended to gather other small specialized companies in the nuclear field under one management umbrella. Yet it didn't develop as well as Will Konneker had hoped. Anticipated financing did not reach his expectations. Neither did accomplishments of the new East Coast executive team. NRD Instrument Company was consolidated with other manufacturing facilities in Denville, New Jersey. Those factors and others prompted Will and Ann Lee to agree on another major career decision. On October 15, 1958, with Bob Allen again serving as their attorney, they bought back the St. Louis operation—using NCA stock they had received from the merger—and formed a new Missouri corporation known as Nuclear Consultants Corporation (NCC). Ken Morganstern, no longer a partner, remained in New York with NCA, and the laboratory in that city was purchased by the man who had been managing it.

Konneker agreed to collect old accounts receivable and solve some other lingering problems for NCA, and by the end of the year, all obligations were concluded. All of the consulting physicists, chemists, lab technologists, and sales and administrative staff remained in their positions under the Nuclear Consultants Corporation banner. Richard Curtin, who managed the labs for Will, remained, as did Barbara Pond, who handled the order desk, shipping room, and traffic responsibilities. (One of the company's earliest employees, Barbara Pond worked previously for Emory Air Freight, gaining experience that proved to be invaluable because of NCA's dependence on airplane deliveries. Not only was she good with figures and invoicing procedures, she also knew intricacies of the transportation system at a time before FedEx, UPS, and similar distribution companies were organized.) Bob Buntaine left NCA and NRD Instrument Company to join NCC as sales and marketing manager. Longtime staff research physicists and chemists, along with consultants, remained in their positions, again under the NCC banner. Curtin, who had been hired by NCA as director of laboratories in St. Louis, switched allegiance, but not responsibilities, accepting a similar position with Konneker. In many ways, the unusual circumstance was recognizable only by changes in affiliations.

If Will Konneker harbored reflective displeasure from the three-year association with NCA, it was not evident in anything he expressed publicly. He simply reiterated his emphatic contention, "It still is my sincere belief that a group of highly trained, research minded people can serve a great need in taking new procedures from basic research programs and engineering them into uncomplicated, reliable, practical techniques that can be profitably employed by the medical profession, industry, and the various branches of government." He resumed building the business, which at that point was 75 percent full hospital laboratory packaging, 15 percent straight radiopharmaceutical sales, and 10 percent industrial consulting.

Unshackled from boardroom hobbles, President Konneker lost little time in reestablishing branch laboratories. Less than a year after NCC's rebirth, he opened a branch facility in the Los Angeles suburb of Glendale to provide medical and industrial services and function as a West Coast distribution center for radiopharmaceuticals produced in St. Louis. Located near the Burbank airport and in close proximity to the freeway system, it was managed by Richard K. Dicky, a University of California graduate, formerly with the L.A. Atomic Energy Project in the field of research and development of film dosimeters and waste disposal.

The next fall, 1960, NCC opened a similar operation on the west side of Cleveland, just a few minutes from the city's municipal airport. Regular shipments of bulk radiopharmaceuticals were received there from St. Louis, repackaged, and distributed to licensed users in northern Ohio, eastern Indiana, Michigan, and western Pennsylvania. In addition, a medical consulting service was initiated, headed by Frank M. Comer, who held a degree in radiation biophysics from the University of Kansas and was former head of the Menorah Medical Center isotope department in Kansas City, Missouri.

Both branches were founded as separate corporations, although the Konnekers owned all stock in the Cleveland laboratory and were 90 percent owners in California, with the remainder owned by lab manager Dicky.

To cover the East, NCC continued to work through the former NCA laboratory at Astoria. The new owner failed to pay his bills, however, and soon went bankrupt. To fill the distribution gap, Konneker quickly set up his own wholly owned branch, this time on Long Island.

Being the first radiopharmaceutical company to establish branch laboratories propelled NCC further into the forefront of that specialized enterprise. Prompt delivery was of utmost importance for short-lived radioisotopes, which obviously could not be stockpiled by hospitals. Major competitors, at that time located on the East Coast and in the South, had late-morning cutoff times for next-day deliveries outside their geographic areas. NCC now covered all four time zones, enabling it to extend those critical deadlines, thus adding to the advantage of its main laboratories being centrally located in a city with excellent airline capabilities. As a result, an order placed by 2 P.M. was guaranteed delivery by 9 A.M. the following day. During periods of bad weather, branch distribution still could provide adequate ground transportation. With such positive results, President Konneker vowed to expand his branch network in the near future.

At the same time, a small, very specialized sales force was being organized within the NCC framework, and in mid-1961, a new division, NUCLEAR, became responsible for development, production, testing, and marketing of a complete line of radiopharmaceuticals. Credentials of NUCLEAR personnel typified those of other employees as well, whether they were identified officially as researchers, consultants, salesmen, or administrators. In addition to having appropriate academic backgrounds and scientific experience, they received considerable company training, and many served in the dual capacities of consultants and salesmen. To gain immediate recognition, the division introduced what was considered the most advanced packaging and labeling in the field. Pricing catalogs listed hundreds of available materials, from a full line of radioiodinated compounds in solutions and capsules to phosphorus, iron, and chromium products, as well as tiny cobalt needles and the necessary lead safes, ranging in weight from a few pounds to a few hundred pounds. (Each safe was designed for foolproof shipping and storage of isotopes. A one-and-a-half-inch hole provided all the space needed to enclose a vial holding hundreds of doses. The remainder of the safe was solid lead.)

A new type of badge, perfected at the Glendale branch laboratory, contained a thin, removable film packet to measure the presence and level of radiation. Worn by personnel working in areas where radioactive materials were handled, the patented badges were sent periodically to the lab, where the films were developed and analyzed by highly trained radiation dosimetry specialists using sensitive instruments previously calibrated with film exposed to known amounts of radiation. Results were reported immediately to clients, with copies kept on file by Nuclear Consultants for future reference, or for evidence if required in courts of law. The film dosimetry business grew rapidly after new state regulations required physicians, dentists, industrial radiographers, as well as other persons handling radioisotopes to subscribe to such a service.

A separate wholly owned firm, the Konneker Corporation, by then was operating a small radium rental company purchased in 1960. The board of directors included Will and Ann Lee Konneker and Bob Allen, who was their attorney on a growing number of projects. The rental service represented a steady, profitable business, but no attempt was made to expand it beyond the St. Louis area. It was, in fact, intended mostly to develop relationships with users of solid-source therapy, for the introduction of a new, safer source.

Looking to the future, Konneker visualized an evolution that would overcome the major drawbacks of radium. Its cost was high. In the form of a powder sealed inside a small platinum needle or cell, it was susceptible to possible leakage, and even a small amount could create health hazards. Taken into the body, it could seek bone structures and remain there permanently. Radium decays into several different isotopes, one being radioactive radon, a difficult gas to contain. Cobalt was being promoted as a possible successor for medical uses of radium, but in its pure form, it could oxidize and flake, likewise causing a contamination hazard.

Constantly searching for improvements in products and savings in costs, NCC researchers developed Cobium, a noncorrosive alloy of cobalt and nickel that could be irradiated to produce radioactive cobalt 60, which they offered as a replacement in clinical applications for radium. As a comparison, the company promoted this exclusive form of cobalt 60 as much safer to handle, without fear of leakage or rubbing off on medical applicators. It was so inexpensive that it could be purchased at prices equivalent to the rental cost of radium. Because Cobium (the new cobalt-nickel alloy) proved to be approximately one million times as corrosion resistant as pure cobalt, the AEC exempted it from usual requirements of sealed sources. As a result, the company soon supplied an estimated 70 percent of the cobalt used for solid source therapy in the United States. "This is one cost of treatment in a hospital that is likely to reduce rather than increase," NCC insisted. President Konneker added what proved to be an accurate prediction that the medical profession's future use of radium would be replaced completely by such products. Although Cobium was cataloged as a radiopharmaceutical, he did not agree with such a designation, because "it requires completely different facilities and personnel for its development and production." The company also developed a cesium 137 compound for industrial uses, a field that was growing as a supplement to its paramount business.

Some major industrial companies seemingly far afield from conventional concepts of nuclear applications gradually were beginning to overcome the inertia of heritage as they looked toward creative new solutions to lingering problems. Will expressed the belief that the future of radioactivity and radiant energy in industry was "almost unlimited," whether a company was engaged in "the production of beer or power." As literal examples, he could point to assignments from St. Louis–based Anheuser-Busch and Union Electric. NCC was, in fact, being hired to untangle an increasing variety of industrial snarls, although it never had advertised that segment of its business either by mail or trade journals, depending entirely on word-of-mouth referrals.

The fatal test-flight crash of an F3H jet fighter was traced to a steel "bucking bar" held inside the skin of the airplane's fuselage during riveting on the outside and forgotten until it damaged vital instruments. Asked by McDonnell Douglas to create something that could avoid the repeat of such a calamity, NCC inserted tiny radioactive cesium slugs into the bucking bars so they could be found easily by a scintillation counter and removed before test flights.

A more complex challenge surfaced with air intakes molded into the fuselages of other early jet naval fighter planes. During takeoffs from carriers, ocean spray sometimes swept through intakes into the jet engines, causing them to flame out and the airplanes to go down. To study the problem, NCC scientists devised a small perforated ring, somewhat resembling a shower head, which they placed in the nose of the aircraft to direct water containing isotopes of gold from a wing tank onto the fuselage, and hence into a jet engine. A trapping mechanism placed at the exhaust of the engine collected small amounts of the water there and measured the effects of preventive steps taken to solve the problem. This enabled engineers to design and install diverters in front of the engines, deflecting the water without obstructing the air intakes.

Inside a California building, radiant heating lines in a very large and exorbitantly expensive floor somehow developed a leak. No one could locate it, including a plumber who drilled tiny holes in numerous locations. As a last resort, the frustrated owner sought help from an NCC scientist who injected very short-life radioactive gold into the lines, applied pressure to force it out at the leak, then rinsed the system, pinpointing the exact leakage spot where the tell-tale gold had left its calling card.

The company utilized radioactivity in many similar instances to tag chemicals or objects, then follow them through processes to problems by detecting the radiation emitted. In other situations, it used high-energy radiation to kill bacteria, change chemical structures, produce physical changes in materials, and penetrate such hard metals as steel for nondestructive radiographic testing or determining the extent of defects. Certain plastics that would melt at moderate temperatures could withstand extremely high temperatures after radiation treatment.

Systems were developed to break down bacteria-resistant grease in sewage disposal plants, keep turbine blades from getting coated with minerals, and show the ultimate disposition of one chemical in Listerine toothpaste. Various contaminants were tagged to determine the efficiency of detergents and other cleansers, as well as techniques, used on materials ranging from clothing to delicate NASA instruments. Elements used in fertilizers were tagged to discover where they were deposited in plants and how well they stimulated growth. Objects such as disposable syringes, sutures, and other medical supplies sensitive to heat were sterilized cold by high-level radiant energy. The use of radioactive tracers made it possible to detect and measure compounds present in a concentration of less than one part in several billions.

A small dolly was constructed to carry radioactive cobalt or cesium capsules down the insides of pipelines in order to X-ray welds. Similar cobalt capsules were put on the ends of Rotor Rooters to trace the routes of sewer lines where records of installations were not available. In each instance, the company was required to get special permission from the AEC to carry out its assignment.

In addition to Anheuser-Busch, Union Electric, and McDonnell Douglas, NCC listed among its industrial clients the Atomic Energy Commission, Emerson Electric, Monsanto, Union Electric, Midwest Piping, General Motors, Dow Chemical, Olin-Mathieson Chemical, Laciede Gas, and Universal Match.

Because the principal objective was to encourage increased use of its radiopharmaceuticals, the company produced most equipment that they sold or leased to existing and new customers as part of a package deal. Although it broadened equipment marketing to all interested purchasers, its major focus was on the medical profession, promoted primarily through major trade shows sponsored by the Radiology Society of America and the Society of Nuclear Medicine. Most members of those groups were physicians, but Will also belonged to the latter organization, serving on several committees and rarely missing a meeting or a show for many years.

To make certain that safety requirements were met in dealing with the rapidly expanding use of radioactive isotopes, Nuclear Consultants expanded its Health Physics Services program for industry and the medical profession. Company physicists made complete surveys of plants such as foundries using radioactive thorium in the production of magnesium alloys, as well as numerous other industrial and medical X-ray and large cobalt 60 installations, to determine possible radiation hazards. They then provided instruction in dealing with problems concerning health physics as related to radiation safety. In addition to AEC requirements, individual states passed regulatory laws governing all types of radiant energy, including X-ray, radium, and radon. NCC was both licensed by the federal AEC to conduct tests and make recommendations and recognized as a "qualified expert company" by individual state lawmakers. Insurance companies called upon the company for expertise relating to radiation safety.

At the beginning of 1962, President Konneker was able to announce a growth of 1,200 percent in pharmaceutical sales and nearly 400 percent in other areas since buying back his company. The full-time staff of twenty-four was supplemented by consultants in biochemistry, pharmacology, radiology, pathology, and internal medicine. All were selected for expertise in their respective fields, and many were associated with various universities and medical schools. A preamble to the presidential report described progress in NCC's medical consulting since its origin:

> During the eleven years of operation, it has been our privilege to help in the establishment of some 500 new nuclear medicine departments throughout the country. These have been located in facilities ranging from small 100-bed hospitals in towns of less than 10,000 population to some of the nation's largest medical schools. The service is designed to offer the skills of well trained medical physicists to small general hospitals that neither require nor can afford such persons as full-time staff members. The services of such a physicist are available for assistance in research projects, the design of isotope or X-ray facilities, calibration of equipment, calibration of X-ray equipment, radiation surveys, or a host of other such services requiring a trained nuclear, medical, radiological, or health physicist.

In 1962, NUCLEAR was the major organization offering all radiopharmaceuticals in precalibrated individual dose vials or capsules. As with other radiopharmaceuticals, these could be sold only to physicians and hospitals that held valid Atomic Energy Commission licenses from suppliers also licensed by AEC. With one of the broadest licenses in the field and with more new radiopharmaceuticals being offered than any competitor, NUCLEAR anticipated a possible doubling of sales within a few years.

Such spectacular growth, the president speculated, would be obtained "only by the considerable expansion of our sales force," which would be "costly and time consuming." He believed it might be more logical at some future date to consider affiliation with an already existing sales force, preferably in the pharmaceutical field, but, for the present, he felt comfortable with the increasing production and sales of his current organization.

Soon after Will Konneker withdrew from the affiliation with Nuclear Corporation of America to re-form his St. Louis company, he and Jonathan Townsend sold their interests in Telray to Marshall Cleland and Ken Morganstern, who moved the company to New York. Although the therapeutic X-ray machine originally planned was not successful, the company, renamed Radiation Dynamics, produced a multi-megavolt accelerator used for electron sterilization, radiation chemistry, and physics research, which did very well.

Parents Roy and Opal Konneker, married in 1918. (Family photo collection)

Will and Winona Konneker in the late 1920s. (Family photo collection)

Fourth-grader Will playing a violin handcrafted by his father. (Family photo collection)

A member of the 1940 McClain High School graduating class in Greenfield, Ohio. (Family photo collection)

United States Army Private Konneker in 1944. (Army photo from family photo collection)

Ohio State University coed Ann Lee Hancock in 1945. (Family photo collection)

Entrepreneurial partners Will Konneker and Ken Morganstern, founders of Nuclear Research and Development, Inc. (NRD photo)

Champion Doberman pinschers, both owned by the Konnekers, earned top awards at a mid-1950s major dog show. Will trained both dogs, which won the female and male competitions, and because he could not show both in the "best of breed" finals, he was assisted by breeder Jack Brown, who sold them their first Doberman. (Family photo collection)

Charles and Winona Konneker Long on their wedding day in 1945. (Family photo collection)

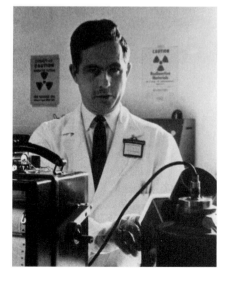

Nuclear physicist Konneker at work in his company laboratory. (Family photo collection)

Nuclear Consultants Corporation main building, designed by company president Konneker, who also supervised its safety-oriented construction. (NCC photo)

With Mallinckrodt CEO Harold Thayer at the conclusion of merger negotiations in 1966. (Mallinckrodt photo)

The former classroom building for Will's classes in his undergraduate major at Ohio University became the first Innovation Center when he directed its organization and operation, beginning in 1983. (Courtesy Ohio University)

Sisters Jane and Ann Lee with popular former Ohio University athlete Pete Lalich, class of 1941, at Homecoming 1983. (Family photo collection)

Malaysian Ambassador Zain Azraai and Will following the 1979 announcement in Washington of an endowed chair named for Tun Abdul Razak. (Courtesy Ohio University)

Washington University Chancellor William Danforth presents a 1991 Distinguished Alumnus Award to Dr. Konneker. (Courtesy Washington University)

The Konnekers and the Pings at Alfredo alla Sarofa restaurant in Rome on one of their frequent trips together. (Family photo collection)

Board members of the Ohio University Fund (later the Ohio University Foundation) at a campus meeting in 1983. (Courtesy Ohio University)

Will with Dr. T. Richard Robe, dean of the College of Engineering and Technology, after conversion of the Innovation Center in 1983. (Courtesy Ohio University)

Surprise on Will and Ann Lee's fiftieth wedding anniversary. (Family photo collection)

With close friend Joan Galbreath Phillips, a 1946 graduate of Ohio University, former chair of the board of trustees, and member of the Foundation board. (Courtesy Ohio University)

8

SPICED WITH VARIETY

*If you are interested, you never have to look
for new interests. They come to you. When
you are genuinely interested in one thing, it
will always lead to something else.*

—ELEANOR ROOSEVELT

On July 11, 1959, Will and Ann Lee Konneker adopted a ten-day-old infant, whom they named Barbara Lynn. Soon after arriving home, they were greeted by one of their closest friends, Barbara Pond, who had lived with them for two years, before her marriage to a member of the Washington University physics faculty. Although she was overjoyed to have the baby named in her honor, she issued an early warning: "Don't call her by her first name. I researched my name of Barbara and discovered it is derived from 'barbarian,' and furthermore, your daughter will always be called Barb or Barbie, or some of the other nicknames I have learned to dislike." With an unsmiling expression revealing the seriousness of her intent, Barbara Pond added, "It is too late for me, but not for her." Ask for a suggested alternative, she immediately replied, "How about B. Lynn?" Unusual, perhaps, but the parents accepted their friend's advice. B. Lynn the name became, and B. Lynn it remained.

Among the youngster's most vivid childhood memories would be those of her room looking out over eighteen acres of wooded countryside and long-distance travels with her parents to attend weekend dog shows. She delighted in both.

Breeding Doberman pinschers had grown from interest in a single pet to a consummate Konneker hobby, providing a gratifying diversion from the rigors of building a radiopharmaceutical business. Friends claimed the experience also revealed one of the couple's salient traits: "Will and Ann Lee never did things half heartedly," said one. "When they became interested in something, they eventually excelled and usually ended up playing leadership roles, without consciously aiming that high."

While living in the Clemens Avenue apartment following graduation from Washington University, Will and Ann Lee had become fascinated by the exceptional training of a friend's Doberman, which appeared to have almost human instincts. They hardly could have imagined that the attraction would influence both their future lifestyles and residential locations, but when they purchased their home in Rock Hill two years later, they also bought a Doberman named Blitz, sparking a new challenge worthy of the dog's name.

The Doberman Pinscher Club of America makes a firm distinction between a dog dealer, who "sells puppies like over-the-counter commodities," and a true breeder, who, "motivated by a drive to create perfection, does his best to educate the people who come to buy dogs and instill in them the ideals and values on which he has built his reputation." The Konnekers made their purchase from such a man, Jack Brown, promising to show the dog, as a condition of the sale agreement.

Although Blitz grew from a promising puppy into a desirable dog, he lacked the star qualities needed for show business. Embarrassed, Jack insisted on giving Will and Ann Lee another dog, free of charge, except that he would retain half ownership. They accepted, received a female named Brown's High Halo (called Trudy), and embarked on the avocation that would bring them great enjoyment for more than two decades.

As a breed with origins in nineteenth-century Germany, the streamlined Doberman, with its sleek, usually dark coat and height of some twenty-six inches at the withers, combines an aristocratic appearance with a high level of intelligence, making it popular as a companion and protector in the home. The American Kennel Club sets standards, as it does for other breeds, that determine breeders' objectives for shows and local clubs. Competitions range from classes for each breed, group classes, and finally the best of each group for the best of show. The Doberman is classed as a "working dog," along with the German shepherd, Great Dane, boxer, and others.

Trudy acted like a member of the Konneker family to the extent that apprehensive friends warned of potential problems stemming from jealousy with a new baby. Instead, Ann Lee said, "Trudy considered B. Lynn *her* baby, and stayed with her all the time, protecting her from any possible danger. She was great."

Trudy not only won her share of trophies, she also produced three litters of puppies after being bred to some of the top males in the country. Each of the joint owners kept one pup per litter, selling the others to carefully selected buyers. Satisfying as success may have been, however, it elicited a temporary downside when a neighbor with political influence convinced city authorities to pass an ordinance against kennels, then define the Konneker hobby as constituting a "kennel operation." Consequently, a uniformed police officer appeared at the Konneker home when Will was at his office. He explained to Ann Lee that she would need a kennel license for the dogs, but since the code was such that a kennel license could not be obtained in Rock Hill, she would have to get rid of the pups. She explained that all the pups would be sold very soon, but they would have to reach a certain age before they could leave their mother. Although he admitted to being embarrassed in being required to follow strict orders, he said the law meant "right away, not in the near future." She replied just as adamantly that she and her husband would not comply until the pups were old enough. Rather than contest the ordinance, however, she and Will began looking for another home. During a six-month search, no further attempt at enforcement was evident, but they had already decided to move. "We were not interested in having a commercial kennel, of course," Will said, "but we enjoyed our hobby and didn't intend to argue with a neighbor or the city government." The house they selected was in St. Louis County, near the suburb of Ellisville, on the remote wooded property they and their young daughter learned to love.

They named their kennel operation "The High Halo Kennels," after their Trudy, and continued showing their dogs. Competitions were divided into two categories: (1) conformation, which Will referred to as "beauty contests, where you make the dog stand still while judges determine which is the most perfect specimen," and (2) obedience in a variety of situations. In training the dogs and handling them at shows, Will concentrated on conformation, and Ann Lee on obedience. Both attended classes to learn their specialties, joined a local club, and did well in selling pups, although they never considered their interest more than a hobby.

Much of Will and Ann Lee's enjoyment came from making close friendships with couples like Mel and Mildred Dold, who shared their interests. The Dolds and Konnekers met at a St. Louis show, where they were presenting their Dobermans. As both families competed at subsequent shows in St. Louis and other cities, their friendship strengthened. After Trudy was bred to one of the country's top-winning male dogs, Will and Ann Lee gave one of the pups, Priscilla of High Halo, to their friends, in a typical arrangement listing the Konnekers and Dolds as co-owners on the American Kennel Club registration papers. The Dolds kept and trained Priscilla, and the two couples shared both competition winnings and money from sales of future pups. Priscilla and many other Dobermans carrying the High Halo name became champions and best-of-show winners.

Junkets to shows led Will and Ann Lee to many major American cities, including Boston, Miami, Dallas, Denver, Chicago, and San Francisco. No matter where they were, neither felt intimidated by professional handlers often hired by competing breeders. As he became increasingly experienced, Will, in fact, did some of the show handling for friends who could not attend, always without compensation, and he succumbed to persistent requests to judge a few specialty events. Mel Dold, who had been an all-American basketball player at Georgia Tech, became recognized as an excellent handler and received a life professional license to show dogs. When his position as a technical sales engineer with Honeywell necessitated a transfer from St. Louis to Wichita, Kansas, he and Mildred continued to show dogs, also opening a kennel for both training and boarding in suburban Goddard. At the Dolds' request, the Konnekers became involved in the venture, too. The couples and their children traveled together regularly, not only to shows but also on summer vacations. All particularly enjoyed canoeing and other outdoor activities at border areas of Minnesota and Canada. Mildred, an energetic woman who always handled the planning, became known as the troop leader, prompting Will and Ann Lee to give her a whistle one Christmas.

Some shows involved hundreds of dogs, which astounded the Konnekers, but they continued to accumulate trophies at local and national levels. Not surprisingly, Will was elected president of the St. Louis Doberman

Club and later served two terms as national president of the Doberman Pinscher Club of America, presiding at meetings and at annual championship events in Miami Beach and Kansas City (1969–70). Mildred Dold was national secretary of the organization during both of those terms.

In spite of their earnest participation, Will and Ann Lee never let their interest grow beyond simply having fun in an activity known to dominate the lives of many who become dedicated dog people. Will insisted they "just loved dogs, liked to see how well we could do with them, and enjoyed the competitive excitement of the shows—rooting for your dog and trying to win, as you do in any sport." When they eventually abandoned the breeding and settled into having just one pet Doberman, Ann Lee acknowledged that the principal motivation for terminating the adventure was her problem of agonizing over every puppy they sold. "Each had its own personality, just like a child," she explained, "and you shouldn't be a breeder when you like them that much." True to the code of the DPCA, however, they maintained enough contacts to follow achievements of dogs that descended from the High Halo lines they had bred.

The one-story house Will and Ann Lee selected near Ellisville, following their long search, had been built many years earlier as the summer retreat of a St. Louis judge. Exposed ceiling beams and a brick fireplace dominated the large living room. Beyond that were two bedrooms, one large and the other very small, a kitchen, and one bathroom. A long screened-in front porch overlooked a creek that followed a winding rural road, appropriately named Kiefer Creek Road. For reasons Will never quite understood, the original owner chose to locate his cottage retreat right in a corner of the eighteen-acre property. There was no garage, not even a driveway, but a small wooden bridge crossed the creek to a gravel parking area, with just enough room for one vehicle. The land, however, was lush with trees, berry bushes, and assorted wild flora. A sizable dry creek wandered down through sloping fields and woods from the nearest neighboring property, located on a five-acre plot at the top of the hill. The judge willed the house to a daughter, who in turn sold it to a real estate executive who bought it strictly as an investment. Someone in that line of owners painted the entire building flamingo pink. Behind it was an abandoned chicken coop that might have been less than attractive if it did not offer the promise of being transformed rather easily into a kennel.

In examining the land, Will and Ann Lee were cognizant of the dry creek, which was just that. Knowing that the area was in a major watershed, they assumed, though, that it would swell considerably with a substantial rain. Making a trip to Ohio for reasons long forgotten, they returned after an extended downpour to find that the creek did contain a flow of water, but without a threat of flooding. Satisfied with all they had seen, they bought the house, vowing to make repainting their first priority. Will soon took care of another priority by converting the chicken house into a kennel with three runs. They also added a driveway and two-car garage with storage space and expanded the small bedroom to meet the needs of their growing daughter.

Through the years, improvements to the house and property added to a fondness the Konnekers felt for their Kiefer Creek home. The porch was made into a long, step-down extension to the living room, with sliding glass doors across the front and sides—an area they considered "a wonderful place to sit and read and enjoy the sun." Will added that you could "watch the cars go by at the rate of about one or two an hour." Even nearby Manchester Road, a major St. Louis artery, was just a two-lane street by the time it reached Ellisville. "You could drive seventy miles an hour on it if you wanted to," Ann Lee said, giving no indication that she chose to do so. Deer, wild turkeys, and "all kinds of interesting birds" were plentiful on the property, she said. As a youngster, even B. Lynn had a private maple tree; whenever she got mad at her mother, she put the family cat, Tinkerbell, on her neck, stomped over to the tree, sat on one of the low limbs, and pouted until the anger went away.

So many changes were made that Ann Lee referred to carpenter George Frenzel as their "live-in contractor." A feisty, independent German, George did not hesitate to argue with Ann Lee, but she remembered that he usually bowed to her wishes. A north wind often swished briskly past the back door, which she said was "the only door anyone ever used," so she asked him to build a small protective extension to the house near that entrance. He vehemently opposed the idea, but went ahead with it as instructed. When she came home from shopping the next day, he was "pounding away with a hammer, as if he were beating out his frustrations on the roof, and I think there were more nails than wood showing when he finished." George always seemed to be in trouble with the union, because he "didn't stand for any nonsense from helpers," firing them on the spot when they didn't meet his expectations. One didn't show up because it was a good day for fishing, so George told him in an uncharacteristically gentle tone of voice, "That's fine; you just keep right on fishing," and never hired him again. Ann Lee praised George as doing "beautiful work," and it appeared to some friends that she even enjoyed the disputations, perhaps because she nearly always won. The home she once referred to as "our funny little farmhouse"—an expression that elicited a scolding from George—gradually evolved like a time-lapse film sequence into the Konneker vision of consummate living, low on ostentation, high on comfort. After having a swimming pool built behind the house, Will suggested that it would be nice to include an adjacent small building for changing clothes. George agreed, but thought it should be a much larger structure. Finding no opposition this time, he built a full guest house with a large living room, dining area, kitchen, bedroom, bath, and sauna. It would prove to be popular, not only as private quarters for visiting friends but also for parties. "Every summer the Bridgers and husbands would have a traditional lobster boil there," Elmer Boehm recalled. "We would have lobsters flown in from Maine, everyone would bring food, as we always did. Will would fire up two big barbecue pits, and Ann Lee would have tables set up all around the pool. It was a great place."

There were some potential glitches, but not many. The municipality of Ellisville announced its intention to annex the Konneker property and levy new taxes accordingly. That riled Ann Lee to the point of temporarily changing her trademark cheery disposition to one of unwavering rebellion. Remembering all too well the city ordinance experience at Rock Hill, she promptly called for assistance from their good friend Bob Allen. Nose to nose once again with city hall, she refused this time to yield. Represented by attorney Allen, she filed a lawsuit against the city, went to court—and won.

Another potential problem arose when the hilltop neighbor, without intentionally meaning any harm, began cutting down small trees and throwing them into the dry creek. Heavy rains then washed the saplings away from his property, depositing them beaver-style in jams that caused the Konnekers' basement to flood. When the neighbor died and his house went on the market, the Konnekers wasted no time in purchasing, renovating, and renting it, thereby increasing their holdings to twenty-three acres and two houses. Although their decision primarily was a defensive measure, and Will was "not enthused with worrying about renters," the result proved to be much better than anticipated. "It turned out beautifully for us and for my parents," said Ann Lee.

Robert and Ada Hancock, Ann Lee's parents, had owned a home at Chautauqua Institute for many years. Before retiring, Robert commuted to operate his charcoal company in Olean, New York, but eventually sold the business and lived full time at the educational center on Chautauqua Lake. Growing restless in retirement, however, the Hancocks sold their home and moved to Virginia, purchasing a bed-and-breakfast complex that included a historic former tourist home and four separate cottages, resting on picturesque wooded acreage between Richmond and Petersburg. Ann Lee remembered it as being "something my mother, a real outdoors person, always wanted to do, and daddy was so easygoing, he just took it in stride."

When the Hancocks decided to retire once again, Ann Lee and Will persuaded them to move into the hilltop house they had purchased a year earlier. "It proved to be a great arrangement," Will said later. "I've heard people talk about in-law problems, but the opposite was true with us. These were wonderful, very capable people, and we had good times together."

Adamant in their resolve to avoid being a burden, Robert and Ada did all their own shopping and driving and tended to the house and grounds themselves, but they never gave the impression of being stubborn. Robert raised a showplace garden and gathered bushels of black walnuts dropping from trees on the property every fall, then shelled them painstakingly during the winter. B. Lynn visited her grandparents nearly every day, helping pick raspberries and peas and eating as many as she picked. Among her fondest memories was "sitting on a little porch swing in front of the house while my grandmother read to me and let me play with her jewelry or brush her hair." Ann Lee said her husband and mother became "the closest of buddies." When snow fell, everyone in the family joined in tobogganing down the hill.

With Doberman and civic interests crammed into the daunting schedule of a burgeoning business, Will Konneker had little room for thoughts of Ohio University, beyond pleasant memories and reading the alumni magazine. He hadn't even been aware of the university's occasional programs in St. Louis until alumni director Martin L. Hecht stopped in to see him at the Manchester Avenue laboratory in the mid-1950s. But that changed when the affable director sold him a $100 life membership in the Alumni Association and convinced him to attend a meeting of the St. Louis chapter. Both Will and Ann Lee (despite her Ohio State loyalty) quickly became active members of the group, which met quarterly in different homes.

As a yearly project, chapter members split into teams to take part in "College Night," a program popular in many cities throughout the country, which lasted a full week in St. Louis. After a full-group briefing by representatives from the campus, teams conducted morning, afternoon, and evening sessions at high schools, telling students and their parents about their alma mater and providing materials furnished by the Office of Off-Campus Relations. "St. Louis alumni fill a real need," Director Hecht reported, "because OU, being a state university, is not permitted to use its own funds to finance out-of-state college nights, even though we receive invitations from cities in several parts of the country." He offered the St. Louis plan as a pattern for other alumni clubs.

Led by cofounders of the chapter—Marlette "Tus" Colvert, one of the top financial officers at Monsanto Chemical Company, and Dorothy Lowrey Vorhees, art director at suburban Kirkwood High School who organized the College Night programs—the St. Louis chapter became one of the most successful in the Alumni Association. "We had a very congenial group and made wonderful friendships that lasted for years, as a result," recalled Mrs. Vorhees, who later became an established water color artist in Chicago, Geneva, London, and Albuquerque and continued to participate in national exhibitions, teach three private classes, and produce annual single-artist shows at the age of eighty-six. "Ann Lee also became a popular member of the group, even though she was an Ohio State alumna, because she had wonderful social skills."

Three years after he joined the chapter, Will, described by Mrs. Vorhees as "low key, but with deep thoughts that he always could articulate well," was elected vice president. In 1964, the national Alumni Association awarded him a certificate of merit "for achieving distinction in nuclear physics."

It became evident in the early sixties that Nuclear Consultants soon would outgrow its leased quarters. Influenced by the critical need for rapid shipping, as well as a larger building tailored precisely to requirements of research, development, and production of radiopharmaceuticals, President Konneker launched a search that ended with the purchase of a property in Maryland Heights, close to historic Lambert Field Airport, twelve miles northwest of the city. Designing the floor plan himself, he made certain the modernistic split-level structure was constructed exactly to his specifications. Although protection had been satisfactory at the leased building, shielding was markedly heightened to assure safe conditions as radioactive projects grew in scope and complexity. After moving to the new location at 2703 Wagner Place in 1963, he unabashedly announced features of what he considered the most up-to-date facility of its kind in the still relatively young business NCC dominated:

- Five different heating and cooling systems controlled temperatures and humidity, according to special needs in areas designed for laboratory procedures.

- "Fume Hoods," each confined to a specific radioisotope to avoid the possibility of cross-contamination, used a separate air supply system operating twenty-four hours a day. Exhaust air was filtered to prevent possible contamination outside the building.

- Blood derivatives and other physiological products were prepared and packaged under aseptic conditions in a sterile room, featuring an air-lock entry and germicidal lamps.

- Iodine 131 products were processed in still another room with a controlled atmosphere (because iodine in certain forms can be volatile), thereby reducing any possibility of cross-contamination.

- Saline, distilled water, and other sterile water products were produced in a room totally free of radioactivity. (Commercially available supplies did not meet the company's strict standards.)

- Bulk quantities of radiopharmaceuticals from production laboratories were separated into individual prescriptions in a dispensing lab.

- A room on the bottom floor was designed specifically to produce the company's exclusive Cobium, its trade name for cobalt

60, which rapidly was replacing clinical uses of radium or radon needles, as the company president had anticipated. (Thin pieces of cobalt wire were irradiated in a reactor to produce radioactive cobalt 60. The wires were cut into small pieces—one-quarter to three-quarter inches—encapsulated in stainless steel needles.)

- Storage vaults extended into the ground, taking advantage of the earth's excellent shielding properties, and distinctive equipment permitted loading and unloading radioactive material from sealed cells and capsules. Special instrumentation guaranteed accurate calibrations and measurements.

- Remotely controlled robot hands behind concrete walls two feet thick manipulated other materials with high levels of radiation in a separate "hot cell" laboratory section.

- A quality-control lab was equipped to check all pharmaceutical products before deliveries to customers.

- Shipping room personnel, headed by a traffic manager, were responsible for packaging and labeling in compliance with strict Atomic Energy Commission requirements and making certain deliveries were geared to the unusual disappearing characteristics of isotopes.

- Office areas included a library and conference room used for staff meetings, in-plant training programs, and product seminars, as well as a resource center for medical physics consultants.

Consulting had more than doubled since 1958, but production of radiopharmaceuticals was outpacing it to the point of representing more than three-fourths of the company's income. Bare financial figures could be misleading, however, because most customers needed professional guidance to keep abreast of escalating knowledge in the specialized field of nuclear medicine. Thus, consulting continued to prime radiopharmaceutical sales that outdistanced those of competitors who concentrated solely on the sale of pharmaceutical products.

Whereas the company once had purchased nearly all raw materials from government sources, it now had to buy additional material from a number of private producers. President Konneker kept in close contact with university and federally operated laboratories doing fundamental research, visiting them and reading papers written by their scientists. "We would pick up this information, hopefully before anyone else, and apply our own technology to transform research-oriented procedures and materials into easy-to-use practical end products for physicians," he said. "All these manufacturing procedures were approved by the Atomic Energy Commission."

The development and improvement of scanners opened a whole new area of diagnostic medicine. These scanners evolved from hand-positioned detectors to machines that could move across selected areas of the body, recording drawings of problem spots by electronically controlled pens moving in consort with detector heads. Lead columnators with pinpoint holes made it possible to focus sharply on targets. (Some years later, the signals would be sent directly to computers, providing another leap in diagnostic capabilities.)

Procedures for radioactively tagging compounds designed to selectively reach specified organs of the body also were attaining levels of sophistication that prompted Will to characterize that advancement as "the next big step following development of the scintillation counter in boosting the company's progress." He considered the combination of enhanced scanning and tagging a good example of physics and chemistry working together in nuclear medicine. The first step was determining, through chemical research, how to produce a drug or compound that would be taken up exclusively by a particular organ such as the lung, heart, liver, or thyroid. Next, the right type of isotope would have to be attached to that substance so its radiation pattern could be tracked and recorded by the scanner. In that way, physicians could monitor the functioning of organs and diagnose abnormalities.

Radiologists, usually in charge of the early hospital nuclear programs, considered this evolution a major breakthrough of the sixties. But it still was difficult to subdue skepticism voiced by habitual naysayers who refused to acknowledge scientists' assurance that injected substances carried only tiny tags of radioactivity, which quickly decayed. In an interview based on diagnostic and treatment properties of radioactive iodine, often preferred because it reacted well as a tag with various compounds, Will Konneker explained, "A doctor can give a patient enough radioactivity to scan a thyroid or some other organ, and administer less radiation than that produced by a chest X ray. But people still cringe at the thought of such a procedure, even though they aren't bothered at all about getting the X ray. Again, it is the word *nuclear* that alarms them."

Such negativism had little effect on NCC's business, because patients were willing to follow doctors' orders. Yet it troubled many medical scientists to realize other substantial benefits to mankind were being stymied by what they recognized as misinformation. Sensationalism that induced public outcries could diminish, or even extinguish, some promising applications of nuclear science. A frustrating example was America's refusal to accept irradiation of foodstuffs—a process in which meats, potatoes, and other basic comestibles were bombarded with high levels of radiation to destroy bacteria. Endorsed by the World Health Organization, the American Medical Association, Mayo Clinic, and other preeminent health groups around the world, it nevertheless was shouted down in the United States, even after companies such as Stone and Webster proved it could be commercialized safely and successfully.

Will's soft-spoken manner perhaps belied his personal feelings on the role irradiation could play in sending food to developing countries, without the need for refrigeration, as well as protecting American consumers from food-related illnesses. Radiation passes *through* the food, he explained, leaving no trace behind, and was "no more dangerous than pasteurization or canning." He described it as a safe, healthful, inexpensive way to enhance food quality and retard spoilage, and he was preparing his company to be ready in case it became a business. Using characteristic subtle humor to make a point, Will sealed a raw hamburger patty in a Ziploc bag, irradiated it at an NCC laboratory, and carried it in a pocket for one month, without refrigeration. He displayed it whenever an appropriate occasion arose, rarely failing to make a favorable impression with his explanation of how the meat kept its red, appetizing appearance. Several years after one such encounter, a man whom he had not seen in the interim came up to him at a business meeting and asked, "Are you still carrying that raw hamburger in your pocket?"

Thirty-five years later, Will would shake his head and exclaim, "It still is hard for me to believe food irradiation hasn't become an important business in this country, as it has elsewhere in the world." In discussing the inclusive topic of radiation, however, he always emphasized the importance of safety. "Of course radiation can be dangerous, whether from the sun or an isotope or an X-ray machine, if precautions against overexposure are disregarded," he said, "but that certainly is true of any kind of overdose."

During much of the sixties, the NCC president served on the Missouri Atomic Energy Commission, a powerful regulatory organization advocating and controlling, when necessary, the proper use of radiation in all its forms. For example, it stopped chiropractors from routinely X-raying an entire body without regard to specific symptoms. "If the whole body needed an X ray, OK, but our commission decided to stop a chiropractor from telling a patient with a sore arm that it would be necessary first to X-ray him from head to toe," Will said. "Such nonsense was expensive and nonproductive, as well as potentially harmful." Similarly, the group put an end to the popular practice of shoe store clerks X-raying the feet of customers.

In 1965, a competitor, Volk Radiochemical of Chicago, merged with a West Coast firm. In addition to selling radioactive materials to the medical profession, Volk had been supplying carbon 14, widely used for research in other fields where an exceptionally long half-life was required. During final negotiations, the new owner, deciding he really didn't want the radiopharmaceutical segment of his acquisition, offered it for sale to Will. An acceptable arrangement was made, and a new branch-dispensing laboratory, Nuclear Pharmaceuticals, was added to NCC's spreading network. The Chicago presence immediately added product volume and improved shipping into northern regions of the Midwest.

Will's earlier thoughts of increasing sales potential through affiliation with a large, well-established corporation subsequently were rekindled in 1965 when one of the city's premiere organizations, Mallinckrodt, Inc., broached the possibility of a merger. The match seemed judicious. The publicly owned company manufactured and marketed a variety of medical products. It had purified the uranium oxide used in the Manhattan Project and supplied the material for fuel to fire commercial nuclear reactors after World War II. Most important to Will Konneker, its large sales force, already familiar with the general concept of medical, industrial, chemical, and radiological product lines, should adapt readily to radiopharmaceuticals. The two companies already served many of the same customers.

Under the Mallinckrodt proposal, NCC would become a separate company division, with Konneker maintaining control as a corporate vice president. The division would continue to occupy Wagner Place facilities, and no change would be contemplated in personnel or executive structure. Konneker would be free to run the company as before, to train and utilize some of the Mallinckrodt sales force as desired, and to continue blending consulting with product merchandising. Branch operations would remain intact.

Negotiations progressed rapidly, and on December 7, 1965, the *St. Louis Globe Democrat* reported on the upcoming merger:

> Harold E. Thayer, president of Mallinckrodt Chemical Works, and Dr. W. R. Konneker, president of Nuclear Consultants Corporation, Monday announced plans for the acquisition of Nuclear Consultants by Mallinckrodt for an undisclosed sum of cash and Mallinckrodt Class A common stock. Nuclear Consultants recently moved to new quarters and is now contemplating further expansion of its manufacturing facility. "Our original estimate was that we would not need further expansion for three to five years," Dr. Konneker said. "We're pushing up against the walls right now." In announcing the sale, Dr. Konneker said that merging with Mallinckrodt will help expand Nuclear's growth by providing increased research facilities and assisting in quality control techniques. Mallinckrodt President Thayer said that the acquisition is a logical extension of Mallinckrodt's pharmaceutical specialty business, particularly the marketing of intravenous X-ray diagnostic agents used by hospital radiologists.

The merger took place on January 1, 1966. Under terms of an unusual agreement, if Konneker reached a specified goal of sales and profit by the end of the first year, no matter what his stock was worth, Mallinckrodt would offer to buy it back for what amounted to twice its price at the time of the merger. If he attained another such goal at the end of the second year, he could sell it back at quadruple the initial price.

Soon after the merger, a serious roadblock appeared when a Mallinckrodt lawyer declared that the branch operations, which Will considered essential to the success of his division, would have to be shut down immediately. The lawyer insisted that they violated FDA regulations and therefore were illegal. No group other than pharmacies, licensed by individual states, was permitted to dilute or break drugs into individual doses. Even though Will's division, like NCC, met all requirements concerning sterility, pyrogens, strength, and other safety standards for injectible drugs, the branches were not licensed pharmacies. Will countered with the argument that the manufacture and distribution of radiopharmaceuticals still was regulated by the Atomic Energy Commission. The Food and Drug Administration was attempting to become involved, but it did not yet have the knowledge needed for tests and inspections. Consequently, it had not yet reached the point of obtaining controls or influencing legality. Following standard FDA test procedures that Mallinckrodt and similar companies were used to for other drugs would be completely inappropriate and fatal for radiopharmaceuticals. The company's top management decided in Will's favor, but the lawyer clung to his opinion for the rest of his life.

Within a short period of time, it became evident that progress of the division would enable it to not only meet but also greatly surpass the established goals. The glamour of the company's "new" nuclear pharmaceuticals business, in fact, would prove to be largely responsible for a marked increase in local and national press coverage, corresponding attention on Wall Street, and substantial gains in the value of Mallinckrodt stock. As a result, Konneker was to find it more profitable to keep his stock than to accept the generous buy-back offer.

At various times, from the sixties and well into the seventies, Will would serve as an adviser to the national Atomic Energy Commission (which became the Nuclear Regulatory Commission in 1974), and a member of the Atomic Energy Forum, an organization representing all companies involved with reactors and their products.

As first chairman of the forum's radiopharmaceutical committee, he worked closely with the federal Food and Drug Administration to establish new regulations for nuclear medicine. The AEC continued to license doctors and medical departments, to assure proper and safe handling, but the FDA became involved with monitoring the products being used as drugs. The result for Mallinckrodt's radiopharmaceuticals division was gaining approval from two agencies, one of which had just entered the scene. Will's committee chairmanship proved to be invaluable for the welfare of his and competing companies, as he candidly explained: "We frankly had to educate the FDA, whose members were accustomed to dealing with long-life, not half-life, drugs. If you followed their existing regulations and procedures, some of the radioisotopes would disappear before the testing could be completed. But we worked together to solve the problems." It was a major undertaking for both the FDA and the radiopharmaceutical industry, but to Will's knowledge, no product the medical profession considered essential was removed from the market because of new FDA policies. Looking back at the experience in a 1974 speech to the Society of Nuclear Medicine, Will noted that "in spite of some mass confusion over who really controlled radiopharmaceuticals, the AEC or the FDA, it was during this decade that nuclear medicine came of age."

Mallinckrodt eventually changed the nomenclature of its branches to "nuclear pharmacies," although the nature of services pioneered by "Dr. K" remained unchanged. As it became firmly entrenched in America's hospital methodologies, this important step in diagnostic medicine led to a specialized segment of the pharmaceutical profession.

As before, Will's business curiosity prompted him to explore another sideline interest, even when he was becoming immersed in new responsibilities with Mallinckrodt. This time it was a small St. Louis specialty restaurant called the Red Lion, which he and Ann Lee liked because they thought it served the best fast-food style roast beef sandwiches in town. Conceived and started by a young IBM salesman named Arthur Morey, it was located near Will's office.

Morey and two co-owners wanted to start a second Red Lion but needed to finance the venture by setting up a separate company. Bolstered by the Konneker reputation for diversity, Morey asked if he would be interested in making an investment in the new restaurant. "Yes," Will answered, "but only if you will also give me part ownership in the one that already is established." The qualification was met, and a second Red Lion soon was opened. Later changed to the Lion's Choice, the restaurant not only would become more successful than the first, but would lead to and beyond a chain in the future.

Will's Aunt Olive died in Greenfield on July 1, 1959, the day B. Lynn was born. His father, Roy Konneker, died in Detroit on June 25, 1966. In addition to Will and Winona and their families, Roy was survived by his second wife, Ruth, and their daughter, Karen, who later married and had three children.

9

DIAGNOSING A MERGER

*Every day you may make progress. Every step
may be fruitful. Yet there will stretch out before you an ever-lengthening, ever-ascending,
ever-improving path.*

—SIR WINSTON CHURCHILL

When brothers Gustav, Edward, and Otto Mallinckrodt formed
a company to produce chloroform, spirits of nitrous ether, car-
bolic acid, bromides, and iodides in 1867, their small St. Louis
plant was constructed below the high-flood water point of the
mighty Mississippi. "We could hardly have picked a more unlikely spot," one of the brothers said later. But that is where G.
Mallinckrodt & Company would remain—at the foot of
Mallinckrodt Street—while it grew into a complex of more
than sixty buildings on forty acres of land, eventually protected by a flood wall.

Incorporated as Mallinckrodt Chemical Works in 1882, the
company progressed into chemicals for photographic processing, then products such as burnt alum, hydrogen peroxide,
tannic acid, barium sulfate, alkaloids, and many others that
followed patterns of the nation's industrial development. It extended production facilities to a branch plant in New Jersey
and sales offices to New York City, entering the twentieth century with a line of five hundred products and a staff that had
grown from four to four hundred.

In the postwar twenties, the company became eminent in the field of X-ray media, and active in the production of medicinal chemicals. It received widespread attention by sportsmen when company researchers developed a fungicide to prevent deterioration of expensive golf course greens, a product that generated sizable revenues for decades. Yet the closely held family corporation operated in the shadow of the St. Louis industrial giant Monsanto Company in terms of public recognition.

That changed considerably after World War II, when the curtain of secrecy was lifted from the Manhattan Project, revealing the company's role in producing high-purity uranium for the self-sustaining chain reaction that led to the atomic bomb and helped usher in the nuclear age. Mallinckrodt thereafter became a leading producer of materials for the Atomic Energy Commission to the extent of briefly threatening to overwhelm other segments of its business in the fifties. In 1954, however, the company initiated a public stock offering and announced a course of further diversification.

At the time Nuclear Consultants Corporation was merged into the company in 1966, Mallinckrodt was beginning to phase out the uranium ore processing activity as it embarked on new quests, including the surge in radiopharmaceuticals. The AEC uranium project, in fact, was to be terminated the following year.

Changes in Will Konneker's business life were barely noticeable during the early years of his new affiliation as corporate vice president and general manager of Mallinckrodt Nuclear. Plans he had been contemplating for expansion of the Maryland Heights laboratories moved forward even more rapidly than anticipated. Construction of an adjacent structure nearly doubled the size of facilities. Then the company bought a nearby box factory, tore it down, and replaced it with a third building twice the size of the other two. Even then, it was pleasantly difficult to meet mushrooming demands for radiopharmaceuticals used to diagnose diseases affecting vital organs, blood, and bones.

Steady improvements in electronic scanners also helped perpetuate the growth cycle, as sales and profits of the division soared far beyond the figures Konneker had pledged. Meanwhile, the allure of what one St. Louis reporter referred to as a "miracle in modern medicine" brought widespread attention to Mallinckrodt Nuclear, both within the company and among media representatives.

Writers seemed particularly attracted to reports involving the handling of an important diagnostic isotope known as technetium 90, valuable for locating brain tumors and other problems because of its short six-hour half-life. The quick decay enabled physicians to inject larger doses, thus obtaining clearer pictures of what was happening inside a patient. "Everyone was searching for a way to use such an element," said Will, "but with a short half-life like that, just getting it across town before it decayed could be a problem."

Brookhaven National Laboratories had provided a possible answer in 1963 by creating what they nicknamed a "molybdenum cow." Using a reactor to make the silver-gray "transition" metal molybdenum radioactive, then placing it in a column and pouring a saltwater solution through it, research scientists could wash out the desired decay product, technetium, a process they referred to as "milking the cow." Konneker's Nuclear Consultants Corporation in turn had become the first to adapt the technique to commercial use, by developing a marketable sterile generator (cow) that could be shipped to hospitals in a special kit for on-site production of technetium. After the merger, the Mallinckrodt division he headed increased that effort, trademarking the product as an "Ultra-TechneKow Generator," but not disavowing its popular nickname. Journalists responded with such lead sentences as "Scientists milk cows every morning at the hospital," and "Each week a herd of cows is shipped from Mallinckrodt Nuclear to hospitals." Never underestimating the power of positive publicity, Konneker cooperated by sometimes referring to the division's herd and calling the shipments milk runs, although he seriously described technetium as one of the principal advancements in the widening use of nuclear medicine. Cost of producing the technetium isotope was less than that of other conventional isotopes, and its chemistry made it an ideal tagging material.

Virtually all isotopes used commercially still were being produced in reactors, such as those at Oak Ridge. Some universities made them in cyclotrons, but only in the minute amounts needed for basic research. When the Atomic Energy Commission cut back on production, Konneker began ordering from a Canadian company (owned and controlled by the Canadian government) that had up-to-date reactors. Having become acquainted with University of Missouri scientists and their problem in financing the operation of a research reactor they had built, he also proposed a win-win arrangement with the physics department there. Konneker's Mallinckrodt division would lease a "hole" in the center of the reactor, where large concentrations of neutrons made it the hottest area, and therefore the most prolific producer of radioactivity. University researchers, more interested in utilizing other parts of the reactor, quickly accepted the proposal, just as their operational funds were nearing exhaustion.

A subsequent advancement Will considered to be another pivotal evolution was the increased use of cyclotrons to make other selected short-life radioisotopes that could not be produced in reactors. Examples were thallium and gallium, which could be injected into blood vessels to provide diagnostic explorations of the heart. Mallinckrodt eventually built two cyclotrons of its own.

On its one hundredth anniversary in September 1967, the company announced a three-for-one split of its common stock, which had zoomed from $70 in 1966 to a high of $170. After the split, it continued to rise steadily. A year later, *St. Louis Globe Democrat* business editor Ted Schafer reported that "the nuclear medical plant in Maryland Heights has had to be expanded four times in the past three years" and that company president Harold Thayer's goal was "to keep Mallinckrodt's growth ahead of the chemical industry, with emphasis on products that offer a distinct user benefit such as harnessing the forces of the tiny atom for the benefit of mankind." Two months later, the company announced that Dr. Konneker was named associate general manager of the entire Pharmaceutical Division, while continuing to head all nuclear activities. A Mallinckrodt publication proclaimed the company's nuclear laboratories "the hub of one of the fastest moving businesses in the U.S.A."

A new facility in Atlanta, Georgia, something Will had planned to set up before merging into Mallinckrodt, now was added to the network of branch laboratories, providing better access to southern markets. It was organized much like those in Cleveland, Chicago, New York, and Los Angeles. Later, the company completed a radiopharmaceutical lab in Carlstadt, New Jersey, and a new customer service center at Maryland Heights.

Konneker considered the therapeutic promises of nuclear medicine "somewhat disappointing," despite a few measures of early success in treating certain cancers before X-ray machines were developed to a high energy level and chemotherapy was greatly improved. Ninety-five percent of radiopharmaceuticals in the late sixties, in fact, were being used for diagnostic, rather than treatment, purposes. Consequently, Will believed the division name should help clarify that distinction. His opinion was reflected in a company bulletin announcing another promotion to a position of wider responsibilities:

> Vice President, Dr. Wilfred R. Konneker, has been named general manager of the newly formed Diagnostic Products Division. In his new position, Dr. Konneker will direct the activities of the hospital marketing group concerned primarily with sales of contrast media and radiopharmaceuticals in the larger hospitals and teaching institutions. In addition, he will be responsible for all of the Company's radiopharmaceutical operations at Maryland Heights, at Sterling Forest, and at the five branch laboratories.

Mallinckrodt had purchased Sterling Forest, a small radiopharmaceutical operation, from Union Carbide Company in the late sixties. The sale, however, did not include Sterling's reactor.

Contrast media, nonradioactive compounds injected into the bloodstream so radiologists can detect (on X-ray film) abnormalities of the heart and the entire vascular system, previously had been marketed with prescription drugs by a separate sales group. They also were sold worldwide through direct exports, foreign subsidiaries and licensing agreements. One of the most promising foreign distributors was Byk-Gulden, a West German pharmaceutical company located in Frankfurt. Mallinckrodt considered it a prime candidate to be the first overseas direct marketer of radiopharmaceuticals.

The German company responded positively to initial overtures but insisted on more than a license or sales agreement. If they could form a separate jointly owned partnership, set up by Mallinckrodt, which also would train managers and employees, a fifty-fifty arrangement would be most welcome. The terms were accepted, and in 1969 Vice President Konneker was on his way to Frankfurt.

The first stage of establishing the new company—dealing with legalities in court—was bewildering, because the law dictated that all proceedings must be conducted in German. Expressions Will had learned in graduate school were adequate for Ph.D. requirements but hardly equal to the task at hand. Despite the linguistic barrier, however, the result was favorable. "Fortunately, my future German partners who were sitting there with me would listen intently to each phrase, and nudge me when it was time to say 'ya,'" he recalled. "Afterwards the administrator laughed and apologized, in near-perfect English, for the strict regulation."

During the time Konneker directed preparations for the start-up of what officially became Byk-Mallinckrodt Chemische Produkte GmbH, he worked closely with Dr. Jurgen Vogal, who had a Ph.D. in chemistry and was selected to head the company. Dr. Vogal moved to St. Louis for six months, observing and participating in Mallinckrodt laboratory projects, before returning to take charge of the joint-venture operation. Konneker, in turn, spent several more weeks at the German plant, completing preparations for what started as a dispenser of products, much like the American branches, but later expanded into a self-contained radiopharmaceuticals manufacturer and distributor.

With the German enterprise solidly in place and prospering remarkably well, Mallinckrodt looked toward Japan, a nation also helping to extend the scope of nuclear technologies but not yet involved commercially in radiopharmaceuticals. Unlike his experience in Germany, however, Konneker initially met resistance in Japan, where the government forbade equal ownership with a foreign corporation. "Fifty-one, forty-nine, yes, but fifty-fifty, no," Will reported succinctly.

Yet Japanese universities were doing research on the medical use of radioisotopes, and business leaders there were anxious to introduce it into the health-related economy. One of the leading pharmaceutical companies, Daiichi Seiyaku, was particularly receptive to the idea of forming a joint venture with Mallinckrodt, for whom it had served for several years as a licensee of contrast media. K. "Dick" Yoshida, foreign liaison officer and assistant to Daiichi's managing director, played a prominent role in negotiations with Will, easily recalling details later:

> We had many legal restrictions against forming an equal partnership in Japan at that time, and there were differences in cultures and systems between the two countries. Therefore, it was a difficult time to reach one-hundred percent understanding in many respects. At each hard negotiation, however, Dr. Konneker's attitude always was to listen to his counterpart's opinion and try to understand the background for conflicting positions. He was very different from

other American executives we had met. He talked softly, was gentlemanly, and respected many opinions, but we felt his deep technical background and innovative nature. Without such support, we might not have concluded successful negotiations.

The result was Japan's first fifty-fifty international joint venture business agreement, creating Daiichi Radioisotope Laboratories (DRL). Dr. Hiroshi Ogawa, who held a Ph.D. in pharmaceutical sciences from the University of Tokyo and was experienced in handling radioactive materials, was named manager, and Dr. Konneker was appointed to the board. Like Dr. Vogal, Dr. Ogawa worked at the St. Louis laboratories for six months before returning to Tokyo to head operations of the joint venture. Dr. Konneker, in turn, made regular trips to help with the start-up, and later check progress of DRL, where he was astounded to discover a typical workday extended from 6 A.M. until midnight.

Tom Boersig, who was with the International Division of Mallinckrodt, often accompanied Will on trips to Japan. Although his primary responsibility was with the company's marketing of such products as contrast media, chemicals, and special golf-course fertilizer in that country, he was described by Will as "a major player" in radiopharmaceuticals, as well. (The two men formed a close friendship that lasted through later years when Tom became chairman of the Japanese subsidiary of Schering-Plough, a worldwide research-based pharmaceutical company, retired from that position, returned to the United States to open a New Jersey office for Daiichi Seiyaku, retired again, and moved to the Country Club of North Carolina, nestled in the famed sand hills near Pinehurst.)

At the end of each visit to Japan, Will was guest of honor at a gala going-away dinner party attended by top executives of both the joint venture group and the parent company. Wives never were included at the dinners, a fact that led to an intriguing situation Will remembered with almost faultless clarity through the years:

> Sometimes, Ann Lee went with me to Japan. Although we arrived at eight o'clock in the morning, several wives were there to greet us, some having traveled two or three hours on the train just to bow and welcome us to their country. The day before leaving for home from one of these trips, Ann Lee, knowing that I had been

invited to a banquet that night, said to Mrs. Ogawa, "I'll see you this evening." When informed that wives never attended the dinners, she replied, "You mean I'll be the only woman there?" Well, someone apparently picked up on that and when we arrived at the banquet, all the wives were there, wearing their finest kimonos. I found many had never even met before, although their husbands had worked together for twenty-five to forty years. The only reason they were at the party that evening was to avoid making Ann Lee feel uncomfortable. It was incredible. I told my wife she had destroyed a custom that might have been a thousand years old.

As in other instances, during numerous reciprocal visits, the Konnekers became close personal friends of Hiroshi and Myoko Ogawa, as well as Dick Yoshida and his wife, Masako. Ann Lee accompanied her husband on some overseas business trips, primarily to Germany and Japan, but also to a trade show in Switzerland.

(Capitalized at fifty million yen, and with fewer than twenty employees, DRI developed steadily, and would reach 1.4 billion yen, with 440 employees in 2002. Meanwhile, Mallinckrodt would sell its share to Daiichi Seiyaku in 1987, ending the joint venture and making DRL a subsidiary of its parent company.)

Eager to accelerate its expansion and diversification efforts, Mallinckrodt next asked Konneker to establish and head a New Ventures Division that could capitalize on emerging fields of technology presenting opportunities for exceptional growth. The challenge was threefold: (1) identify commercial opportunities from new scientific developments; (2) enter new fields through internal developments, acquisitions, and licensing arrangements; and (3) operate these businesses through their initial stages.

Shifting for the first time in his business career from direct supervision of producing radiopharmaceuticals he had introduced to the world nearly twenty years earlier, Konneker described his new staff in January 1970 as "myself, one other physicist [John Jarvis], and a secretary," but he was free to recruit employees from the entire company to work on specific programs. After defining and studying his new objectives, he launched a program to detect business opportunities that could be linked to what he considered the most promising advanced technologies as they emerged.

During the next three years, Will traveled nearly 150,000 miles annually, screening and purchasing small technically oriented companies, primarily health related, that were changing management, in need of financing for expansion, searching for qualified salespersons, or in other ways positioned to benefit from mergers. (He confessed to being in the air so much he abandoned personal small-plane flying he had been pursuing "just for fun.") Two of the earliest companies acquired through his program were Serosonic Laboratories of Long Island, New York, and Diagnostic Science in Orlando, Florida, providing a base to enter the clinical diagnostic reagent marketplace.

Konneker believed strongly that consulting services of the pharmaceuticals group he formerly headed stimulated product sales. It was a philosophy he had embraced since forming his own company in 1950. For that reason, he was disappointed to learn after he moved to New Ventures that consulting was being phased out to avoid a possible conflict of interest with overall sales efforts. The company, in fact, simply turned the consulting portion over—without charge—to Paul Early, a good friend of Konneker who had worked for him in the Cleveland office. (Ten years later, Mallinckrodt paid a handsome sum to buy the business back from Early.)

In the early seventies, as an aside to his Mallinckrodt employment, Dr. Konneker joined two young St. Louis engineers, Warren Kinninger and John Beld, both graduates of Washington University, to form a company they named Infa-Care, Inc. Although hospital intensive care units were improving facilities regularly for adults, incubators for premature babies were not yet available. Working with a pediatrician at St. Louis University Hospital, Kinninger and Beld had been attempting to fill such an obvious void. At their request, Will invested in becoming a part owner, as well as helping them complete the development of a totally sterile neonatal intensive care assembly capable of controlling the environment surrounding a baby while continuously monitoring all vital signs. The equipment, an instant success with sales to hospitals throughout the land, was built and marketed by the Infa-Care founders for several years, then sold to Pioneer Corporation of Kansas City, Missouri, where it became a separate division.

Since 1968, Konneker also had become increasingly active as a member of Ohio University's Alumni Board of Directors, being elected vice president in 1971 and president two years later. In addition, he began a long tenure on the University Fund Board in 1972.

Will and Ann Lee by then had become life members and annual benefactors of Washington University's William Greenleaf Eliot Society, founded in 1959 in tribute to the institution's cofounder. The society provided unrestricted major gifts, regularly representing more than half of the total annual giving income. Its success through the years contributed substantially to the university's development.

Primarily through that connection, a friendship developed between Will and Washington University's alumni director Allen Martin. Actually, they had met when Allen's daughter received a degree from Ohio University at a commencement where Will welcomed new graduates to the university's Alumni Association. That coincidence had been forgotten, however, until it arose when the two men began having frequent lunches together in St. Louis. A more serious topic at those lunches became their mutual belief that the time had come to provide a lasting tribute to Arthur Llewelyn Hughes, the former physics department chairman, whom Will greatly admired. When talk progressed to action, Allen moved to the Central Development Office as director, so Will worked with the College of Arts and Sciences in mapping out a fund-raising plan to remodel a large area of the Crow physics laboratories building into a major classroom in honor of Dr. Hughes. Will sparked the resulting drive by offering $100,000 as a matching gift, then helping to raise a like amount to complete the financing for what became the Arthur L. Hughes Lecture Hall. (Hughes died in 1978 at the age of ninety-five.)

Despite his diversity of interests, Will always dismissed urgings of friends who thought he should become involved in politics. The most enticing of these was proffered by Christopher S. "Kit" Bond, the Missouri state auditor who was campaigning for the governorship in 1972. Ann Lee had known the candidate's wife, Carolyn, through their work with Chi Omega sorority, leading to a friendship between the two couples. The Bonds had been houseguests of the Konnekers at Ellisville, sharing discussions on many subjects, including business, arts, and political affairs.

Following Kit Bond's November election as governor, Will received a telephone call from Robert James, another friend, who was in charge of the statehouse transition at Jefferson City. "Governor Bond is putting together his cabinet and would like to have you visit him," James said, declining to explain details of what was to be discussed. Will accepted the invitation, as much from curiosity as friendship, and drove to the capital city. There the mystery unraveled: Governor Bond wanted him to consider becoming director of the Missouri Department of Revenue. Admitting the flattering offer presented a tempting challenge, Will asked for time to consider it. But by the time he arrived back in St. Louis, he was certain of his decision. In a follow-up letter thanking the governor for the compliment, he wrote, "I am most honored that you would consider me for such a position within your administration . . . I did some real head scratching and thinking after our discussion, but finally called Bob James and asked that my name be removed from consideration at this time." Reminiscing many years later, Konneker said, "That was the closest I ever came to getting into politics, and it was as close as I have ever wanted to be." (Republican Kit Bond was elected to the U.S. Senate in 1986 and reelected for two more terms, with the next election due in 2004.)

With growing involvement in myriad outside activities, all of which were important to both Konnekers, Will asked to be relieved of full-time Mallinckrodt responsibilities in the spring of 1973. "Consistent with his request," the company announced, "arrangements have been made for him to serve in the capacity of a half-time consultant." Board Vice Chairman Harold A. Brinner explained: "As in the past, Dr. Konneker will assist the company in identifying commercial opportunities for new scientific developments and entering new fields through international developments, acquisitions, and licensing arrangements. While the company regrets the need for Dr. Konneker to devote more time to his outside personal interests, we are pleased that he will be available on a half-time basis to assist in the company's development programs."

The next nine years were to add a potpourri of family, personal business, university, hometown, and Mallinckrodt episodes that would keep the Konnekers wondering themselves how they were able to keep up with their self-imposed schedules. Will made regular trips abroad for Mallinckrodt, determining the overseas extent of nuclear medicine utilization, helping to set up a new manufacturing company in Germany, and continuing to serve as technical liaison there, as well as in Japan.

One of his most interesting consulting assignments during that time was to explore the possibility of organizing a radiopharmaceutical marketing system in Brazil. A multilingual Mallinckrodt salesman who covered that territory, along with Spain and Portugal, recommended South America's largest country as a "red-hot prospect." Brazil was, after all, the fifth largest nation in the world and had common boundaries with six of the other eight countries on the continent.

At first glance, Will tended to agree with the salesman's assessment. Flying to Rio de Janeiro, he talked with doctors, businessmen, civic leaders, and many others, all of whom favored the idea. Brazil at that time seemed destined to become an economic power. Skeletons of rising business structures throughout the city gave promise of an economic boom. Many more new buildings were being planned. Equipment for what was projected to become a modern new hospital already had arrived in large crates at the building site. Yet the likelihood of competition in the field of radiopharmaceuticals seemed almost nonexistent.

Back in St. Louis, Will met with company officers, who agreed to sidestep any idea of a joint venture, such as those in Germany and Japan, and start with a branch laboratory to separate and dispense products shipped from Maryland Heights. The plan was initiated, and during the next few years, the new subsidiary, Mallinckrodt Productos Diagnosticos e Quimicos, Ltda., began to build a substantial business.

Will made occasional trips to observe its progress. What he concluded, however, was that the country was becoming mired in a morass of gross inefficiency and government problems. Five years after his first trip, the hospital equipment still was in crates. A restaurant on the top floor of one of the skeletal buildings had been opened, but none of the structure below it was finished; he and some friends had to take a freight elevator through the frameworks of areas where lights were hanging from cords and walls were not yet installed. When they finally arrived at the dining room, waiters refused to serve them until they had finished watching a soccer game on television.

Most important, inflation was so out of control—nearly 100 percent—that people used up Friday paychecks to buy commodities immediately, because they would be more valuable by Monday. Radiopharmaceuticals sold well, but by the time the currency could be exchanged into dollars, it had plunged in value. Finally, Mallinckrodt surrendered to the hopelessness of the situation and withdrew. "Somebody might have tried to revive the business in later years," Will said, but he never looked back to see.

Shortly after Konneker's consulting agreement ended in 1982, Mallinckrodt was acquired by Avon Products. Four years later, Avon sold it to International

Minerals and Chemical Corporation, which later changed its name to IMCERA Group, Inc. The following two decades brought a series of decentralization, acquisitions, a name change from IMCERA Group to Mallinckrodt Group, mergers, splits, and partnership ventures. On October 17, 2000, Tyco International Ltd., a diversified manufacturing and service holding company headquartered in Bermuda, announced its purchase of Mallinckrodt for approximately $4.2 billion. The Maryland Heights laboratories Konneker had built for his original company, and which were expanded several times thereafter, still produced enough radiopharmaceuticals to represent a substantial percentage of company sales.

PART II

THE ENTREPRENEURIAL TOUCH

Next in importance to freedom and justice is popular education, without which neither freedom nor justice can be permanently maintained.

—JAMES A. GARFIELD

Wilfred Konneker with Dr. Thomas Wagner and his wife, Tong. (Courtesy Ohio University)

Daughter B. Lynn in competition. (Family photo collection)

Bride-to-be B. Lynn makes certain her father is ready for the wedding. (Family photo collection)

Will and Elmer Boehm slip into a photograph of the St. Louis "Bridgers." From left: Bonnie Braddock, Jan Boehm, Ann Lee, Jo Rausendorf, and Carolyn Brown. (Family photo collection)

Good friends get together in Japan. From left: Myoko and Hiroshi Ogawa, Ann Lee and Will, K. "Dick" and Masako Yoshida. (Family photo collection)

The Konnekers met Colin Powell at a Washington University Foundation Day program shortly before the retired general was appointed U.S. secretary of state. (Family photo collection)

Jack Ellis and Will check a fund drive agenda. (Courtesy Ohio University)

At the celebration dinner for the 1804 Fund campaign, from left: Sue and Jack Ellis, Ann Lee, Charles Ping, Will, Claire Ping, Jean and Bob Axline. (Courtesy Ohio University)

At a Sheldon Concert Hall performance in St. Louis, Sheldon board chairman Gloria White, singer Tony Bennett, Ann Lee, Will, and nationally acclaimed New York photographer Herman Leonard, a 1947 Ohio University graduate. (Family photo collection)

The Konnekers join Metropolitan Opera mezzo-soprano Denyce Graves following a performance at the renowned Opera Theatre of St. Louis. (Family photo collection)

Ohio University president Robert Glidden addresses the audience at the 1996 dedication of the Konneker Research Laboratories on The Ridges. (Courtesy Ohio University)

The Websters—Cara, Bill, B. Lynn, and Trey—in 2003. (Family photo collection)

Will and longtime Konneker
Development Inc. secretary Sue
Winter. (Family photo collection)

The W. R. Konneker Alumni Center. (Courtesy Ohio University)

10

DEFINITIONS OF DESTINY

You can't build a reputation on what you are going to do.

—HENRY FORD

An American biographer once observed that with all due respect to advance planning, patterns of family lives evolve more through unexpected than anticipated outcomes of venturesome acts. The Konnekers could hardly disagree.

In the summer of 1967, a year after Will had sold his company to Mallinckrodt, he and Ann Lee attended a banquet sponsored by Arts in Education, one of several St. Louis nonprofit groups they had begun to support. To help raise money for various fine arts causes, the annual gala featured an auction of items donated by local enterprises. Whether inspired by thoughts of his own youth or simply caught up in enthusiasm for the cause, Will could not resist responding when the auctioneer announced the Three Rivers Stable's donation of a white Connemara pony, an Irish-bred animal the size of a fullgrown horse. Others joined the bidding, but it became obvious Will was going to get that pony for his eight-year-old daughter, B. Lynn. The next day, a delighted daughter was taken into the tack room of a nearby Ellisville stable to discover her new pony, River Mist.

"Buying that big pony proved to be one of the best deals we ever made," Will insisted. "B. Lynn rode and rode and rode, and then got into hunting/jumping competition that became her major passion and an important segment of our family interests as well." After a period of overlapping equine/canine pursuits while Will headed the Doberman Pinscher Club of America, the pony gradually gained precedence.

B. Lynn began to ride daily after attending classes at Principia, a private Christian Science–affiliated school. "My mother took me to school every morning, because there was no bus," she recalled. "Before we left, it was my job to have my riding clothes and shoes in a brown paper sack at the door, so she could bring it when she came back for me at the end of the school day, took me directly to the barn, and waited while I rode and took care of my pony. On weekends, one or both parents took me to ride on Saturday and after church on Sunday. Fortunately for them, when I got a little older, they could just drop me off at the barn, rather than wait there, but either way it was an incredible sacrifice—the kind you really only appreciate later."

The Connemara breed of pony is known for its hardiness, agility, and extraordinary jumping ability, as well as its size. When B. Lynn advanced to middle school and high school at Principia, she became a regular participant at local horse shows, then on the national "A" Circuit of the American Horse Shows Association, winning awards in progressively higher divisions. After finally putting the pony out to pasture, she continued to win trophies with a succession of horses, most of them thoroughbreds converted from racers to hunter/jumpers. But she never sold River Mist, preferring to keep him with some farm friends, and he lived to the age of thirty-five.

B. Lynn attended Mary Baldwin College in Stanton, Virginia, then transferred to Culver Stockton College in Canton, Missouri, where she was graduated in 1983. During those years her equestrian fervor never waned. Rather, it was further heightened when she became interested in dressage—the use of slight movements to control a horse—and a friend, Joanna Walker, whom the Konnekers had met at dog shows, suggested that she go abroad for British Horse Society training. In addition to showing dogs and judging shows, Joanna was an expert horsewoman born in England and now living in North Carolina. The hope was realized when Will and Ann Lee gave their daughter financing for three months at a society-approved training center in Somerset County, England, as a graduation present.

As a student at the center, B. Lynn followed a daily regimen of riding and grooming horses in the morning and afternoon, followed by studying equestrian-oriented textbooks in the evening. Before the end of her initial training, she obtained jobs at a stable and in a restaurant, enabling her to remain in England, compete in hunting and jumping events, and take a series of British Horse Society examinations leading toward internationally recognized professional training qualifications. With her parents cooperating again by buying her an Irish Warmblood show jumper, she did well both in competition and with exams, until deciding to return home in 1986.

Will Konneker's association with Mallinckrodt, coincidentally, virtually paralleled the time his daughter was in school. With the stream of personal and business transitions taking place during those years, the decade of the seventies might well have been the busiest in the lives of the family.

While Will was carrying out his consulting missions, the Lion's Choice chain began a steady but exceedingly conservative growth. Each new restaurant was opened only after the company could free sufficient cash to completely finance buying a lot and constructing and equipping a building. As a major shareholder, second only to Art Morey, who founded the company, Will pushed for more aggressive growth, reasoning that it should reach an overall value making it highly attractive to possible purchasers when an appropriate time came for liquidation. His idea was not immediately popular among other owners, but over a long period of time they finally accepted a plan of long-term financing. Before the end of the century, the chain would reach fifteen restaurants, most of them in the St. Louis area, and soon afterward, a franchise program would be set in motion.

In 1974, the Konnekers were catapulted into yet another new venture, this time in the world of sports, when Art Morey introduced Will to an enthusiastic friend with a speculative proposition. Charles "Chuck" Spaulding wanted to build a racquetball club. Racquetball, a relative newcomer in athletics, had been created by a tennis pro in 1947. Combining the rules of squash and handball, it had gained a measure of early respectability but had not shown great potential until 1968, when a group of players founded the International Racquetball Association (forerunner to the American Amateur Racquetball Association). Suddenly, the sport had a uniform set of rules, specially designed equipment, and a following that seemed destined to create a national craze. Chuck Spaulding, whose name often was confused with Spalding, the well-known sports equipment manufacturer, was eager to build the first racquetball club in St. Louis, if Konneker would purchase enough initial stock to make it possible.

Will became convinced that the concept had a financial future but hesitated to invest in stock. "If the company goes under, I will simply lose the money," he told Spaulding. "Instead, I am willing to construct the building, lease it to you, and take a percentage of the income; that way, if it doesn't work out, I will at least own a building." The plan was accepted, and within six months the city had its first six racquetball courts (later expanded to eight) in a new brick building on Enchanted Parkway in Manchester. Almost simultaneously the mania struck as expected. Konneker built a second club north of the airport and expanded his interest by becoming involved in Racquetball Clubs operations. Then he and Spaulding sought others who would follow the pattern of constructing facilities, which the company would rent and manage, always paying percentages of profits. When St. Louis became dotted with Spaulding clubs, Will built one in Kansas City, using it not only as another successful operation but also as a pump primer for other investors to erect and lease facilities. He combined the three he owned outright under Konneker Development Corporation.

The late seventies and early eighties brought a hefty surge in sales of racquets, number of players, and demands for new clubs across the country and in other nations. A U.S. team won the first Racquetball World Championship tournament held at Santa Clara, California, in 1981, giving the sport increased worldwide prestige. Meanwhile, Konneker organized a partnership with several friends and other investors to buy a property and construct a large facility at Fort Lee, New Jersey. It, too, prospered, although not to the extent of the others, which often had to be expanded to keep up with business. At the height of the company's success, Spaulding was managing forty clubs across the country. Overextended in both workload and financing, however, Chuck Spaulding suddenly withdrew without notice. Mark Beckham, serving as the equivalent of chief financial officer, quickly put together a new management company, picking up business from some of the owners who did not want to assume active supervision.

Will chose to hire his own managers, as well as an overall supervisor, and operate the clubs he owned directly through Konneker Development Corporation. When the supervisory approach crumbled, Will and his secretary, Sue Winter, who had been with the racquetball group since 1977, were left with direct operation of the business. "She was invaluable," he said, "better than any supervisor I could have hired." Yet he believed the public fanaticism would subside, even though the sport itself would continue to be popular among athletics devotees. A clue, he noted, was that players were standing in line from 4 P.M. to midnight but not appearing much during the mornings and early afternoons. Having enjoyed the successful adventure, he nevertheless concluded it was time to withdraw. Where he once had owned the only club in St. Louis, the city now had thirty-three.

Consequently, he offered for sale the three clubs he owned outright, along with the partnership venture in New Jersey. The latter was sold to a developer who converted it into an office building, as racquetball clubs indeed became overbuilt and began to falter. Sales of the two clubs in St. Louis and the one in Kansas City followed, although with some difficulty, but he preserved Konneker Development Corporation as an umbrella for his other diversified activities. Through an arrangement with the new owner, Will and Sue Winter even remained in an office he had added to his original Enchanted Parkway building. During future decades, Sue would become increasingly involved as an executive secretary, and as a personal confidante of Will, Ann Lee, and their family.

Looking back, Will analyzed his racquetball involvement: "It was a very good business, and lots of fun, but it was time to get out. In fact, I probably could have done better by getting out a little sooner, but you can't expect to forecast exact peaks or valleys in the investment business." One of his closest friends insisted success of the speculative venture exemplified "Will's remarkable sense of timing in making business decisions."

Many owners of racquetball clubs were able to survive the eventual demise of their ill-fated businesses by converting the buildings to health fitness centers, which became the next American obsession.

As a member of the Ohio University Alumni Association and Fund boards in the early seventies, Will Konneker witnessed the sense of disarray that plagued American higher education. Students across the country protested what they perceived as a senseless waste of life and youth in a useless Vietnam War. The problem, which had been compounded in May 1970 when demonstrators were killed at Kent State (Ohio) and Jackson State (Mississippi) universities, led to formation of a Commission on Campus Unrest, appointed by President Richard M. Nixon. Its conclusions did nothing except to place the nationwide blame on a combination of fanatical student tactics, complacent campus officials, and ineffective law enforcement.

Ohio University President Claude Sowle, who succeeded President Vernon Alden in 1969, had arrived just before the problems escalated into destructive action. Less than a year after his inauguration, angry students attacked his home and shouted abusively at him, gestures described by a university trustee as "indiscriminate protesting." Campus discipline collapsed completely on the morning of May 15, 1970, when, for the first time in the university's history, classes were shut down, not to reopen until the beginning of summer sessions.

Problems of the early seventies were further exacerbated by situations unrelated to protests. The state of Ohio eliminated a subsidy for out-of-state students, and several colleges in northeastern Ohio came on line as state-supported institutions, drawing away potential students from an important marketing area. Enrollment dropped from nearly 20,000 to 13,000. Individual colleges within the university became rivals in competing for their shares of diminishing budgets. Jack G. Ellis, then director of development, with administrative responsibilities also for alumni affairs, exclaimed, "People on campus were walking around with little dark clouds over their heads."

At this low point in the university's recent history, Will Konneker was elected president of the National Alumni Association. "There wasn't much consolation in knowing these kinds of troubles had been plaguing most of the country," he said. "It had approached anarchy, and it naturally hurt our association, because the situation was difficult to explain when alumni were reading and viewing negative media reports. There wasn't much we could do, except help wherever possible in efforts to turn it around." (Jack Ellis had been castigated, almost physically, when he attempted to defend the university's position at an alumni gathering in New York City during the height of the tension.)

Following the resignation of Claude Sowle in 1974, Dr. Harry B. Crewson, a highly respected member of the economics faculty since 1949 and a civic leader in Athens, was named interim president while trustees sought to identify someone who could lead Ohio University out of its doldrums. During his temporary tenure, Dr. Crewson drew high praise from both the university and city communities for mending wounded spirits of hope and cooperation to help ease burdens of transition for a new president.

As alumni president, Konneker became a member of the search committee to find the university's eighteenth president. After interviewing possible candidates across the country, committee members overwhelmingly agreed to recommend Dr. Charles J. Ping, provost of Central Michigan University. Getting him, however, would not be an easy accomplishment.

A graduate of Southwestern University and the Louisville Presbyterian Theological Seminary, Ping had received a Ph.D. from Duke University. He was a full professor of philosophy, as well as provost, at Central Michigan and had lectured six summers at the Harvard University Institute for Educational Management. At the time he was contacted by Ohio University's search committee, Ping was attending the Harvard Advanced Management Program, with expenses paid by Central Michigan's board of trustees. Meanwhile, he was being urged to become a candidate for the presidency of Central Michigan, a position being vacated by William Boyd, recently named president of the University of Oregon. Ping twice insisted that he was not interested in being considered for the Ohio University presidency, but finally agreed to meet with search committee representatives in Boston. Greatly impressed with that meeting, he made several inquires about the university among educators he knew at Harvard and elsewhere, receiving a mixture of opinions ranging from high praise to negative comments. As a result, he and his wife, Claire, visited Athens to make their own determination. "We liked the setting, and the people we met gave us the feeling that it would be an excellent place to be," he recalled later. Among those they met was Will Konneker, who had not been with the committee group that flew to Boston. "He certainly was part of the influence in my decision," Ping said.

Elected unanimously by the board of trustees, Dr. Ping was inaugurated as the university's eighteenth president on September 1, 1975. That fall, he and Claire were introduced to alumni during a round of visits to chapters across the country. The meeting at St. Louis further enhanced a friendship destined to grow increasingly warm between the Pings and the Konnekers.

President Ping identified the university's most immediate objective as recovering the self-assurance it had lost through fiscal problems, bad press, and declining enrollments. Student recruitment, faculty enhancement, curricula magnification, and administrative restructuring became keystones of plans he incorporated in a mission statement for the next ten years. Speaking with candor soon recognized as a mark of his modus operandi, he challenged the university community to decide whether as a body it would "move toward reinforcing these commitments or be lost in the backwash of defensive bickering, party strife, and adversarial dealings." He personally met regularly with deans and faculty/administration groups, emphasizing a teamwork approach to solving problems, and sought to reinforce cooperative programs with business, industry, and social organizations throughout the area and abroad. And he turned to alumni and friends for increased assistance in extending major financial boundaries that always limit a university's budgetary profile.

As a start, President Ping and Jack Ellis, who by then was executive director of the Ohio University Fund, sponsored a weekend retreat with several supportive alumni in the state to explore the feasibility of organizing the university's first capital gifts campaign. When the sad fact was revealed that there wasn't enough seed money to even start such an ambitious project, two retreat participants, industrialists C. Paul Stocker and Fritz J. Russ, both distinguished graduates of the College of Engineering, pledged the necessary cash. "The 1804 Capital Gifts Fund Campaign" was selected as a name, reflecting the year of Ohio University's birth, with the appeal focused on positive aspects of its history and its future. The all-important initial steps would be forming a steering committee and choosing a dynamic campaign chairman.

At first, Ellis noted, it appeared that Mother Nature was opposed to the idea. Severe snowstorms throughout the area in the winter of 1977–78 repeatedly stymied scheduled steering committee meetings. On one such occasion, only Fritz Russ, from Dayton, was able to make his way to the campus. Finally, after several postponements, Columbus realtor John W. Galbreath offered his winter home at Lagorce Isle, Florida, for a meeting place. The meeting, held in January 1978, was attended by a group of men representing boards of trustees, alumni, and the fund, all of whom had proven their loyalty and support for many years. Jack Ellis, President Ping, and Wayne Kurlinski, who recently had joined the administrative staff as vice president for university relations, were with them. Ellis noted and long remembered the proceedings:

> Our strategy, quite honestly, was to ask Warren McClure, a vice president and major stockholder of Gannett Publishing, to be our chairman. He had the dynamics to lead such a campaign. Everyone there seemed to agree about that, but at the appointed moment for his nomination, he informed us that current business with the newspaper chain made it impossible for him to accept such a commitment. He would give a million dollars, however, for turning it down. That was one of the best declinations I have ever heard, and we accepted it, of course, but we still were without a chairman. At that point, Will Konneker excused himself and left the room for a few minutes. When he returned, he learned that we had nominated and elected him chairman of the 1804 Campaign. We were delighted when he accepted the job, although he vowed never to excuse himself from another meeting of that group.

During the campaign that followed, Konneker proved to be much more than a titular head of the drive. He worked closely with Ping and Ellis, first in identifying prospective large donors, then traveling the length and breadth of the country seeking a substantial number of firm commitments to announce at the official kickoff, scheduled for the fall of 1978. A goal of $14 million was set for the total campaign, expected to last three years.

Paul Stocker, founder of Lorain Products and one of the most generous supporters in the university's history, had agreed enthusiastically to join the effort. He and his wife, Beth, had in fact promptly pledged $3.3 million and anonymously financed costs of developing promotional materials for the drive. However, Stocker died on August 23, 1978, just two months before the official opening. In addition to the initial pledge, his will, bequeathing several types of endowments for the university, provided so much more for the 1804 Campaign that when public announcement of the upcoming drive was made in the Columbus office complex of Nationwide Insurance President Dean W. Jeffers (a 1936 graduate of Ohio University), 90 percent of the projected goal already had been reached.

This included the planning session commitment Warren McClure kept and other early major contributions.

Konneker continued to travel with Ellis, reaching out to several thousand alumni and friends, even though he still was going abroad as Mallinckrodt's consulting liaison, directing extensive surveys of universities and medical centers in Japan and Europe to determine the status of diagnostic medicine. "Although it was somewhat of an exaggeration, we sometimes shuddered to realize that at times we might have been spending more time with each other than with our wives," Ellis said, "but I was doing it as a hired hand, and Will was doing it as a volunteer."

Faculty members and administrators also joined in, making inordinately high commitments that drew flattering comments from development officers at other universities and provided further inspiration among alumni, corporations, and foundations. Will provided $10,000 to commission Don Whitlatch, official naturalist artist for the state of West Virginia, to paint a special full-body bobcat so that limited-edition prints could be sold to alumni and friends. Lawhead Press, Inc., of Athens, selected to make the complex four-color-plus prints, later announced it was contributing them to the campaign. Unveiled at homecoming in 1981, the original painting remained on display in the Convocation Center.

As part of their contribution to the campaign, Will and Ann Lee Konneker wanted to finance the purchase of an alumni house that could become a prominent campus landmark. The need for a dual-purpose building that could provide office space and serve as a welcome center for visiting alumni had been discussed often during the time Will served as president of the alumni board. His wife suggested that the current campaign made the timing just right to make the move. Alumni offices in the past had been in Cutler Hall and then in Lindley Hall, which had been converted from a women's dormitory into quarters for a variety of administrative offices. "You really had to search for the alumni staff members at Lindley," Will noted.

Will, Ann Lee, and Jack Ellis investigated several properties on the periphery of the main campus, but none met the desired criteria. Finally, through his leadership in the fund drive, Will discovered that the historic Grosvenor House directly across University Terrace from the main campus might become available. Built at the turn of the twentieth century for Brig. Gen. Charles Grosvenor, a Civil War veteran, lawyer, state representative, and U.S. congressman, it remained in that family until the general's granddaughter, French Professor Emerita Constance Leete, donated it to the Episcopal Church of the Good Shepherd in 1967. The church had used it for Sunday school classes and leased a portion to Ohio University for use by the philosophy department and the Black Studies program. Remembering the imposing red brick home with massive white pillars from his days as a student, Konneker considered it a perfect fit. It could be converted into an alumni house without too much trouble, and alumni could drop in, relax, and get information.

Negotiations with the church were successful, and on June 6, 1980, a planning committee began what would become a series of meetings extending through the following eighteen months. Members who would oversee renovation of the house included the Konnekers, Claire Ping, Barry Adams, Rose Rutherford, and John Jones. Director of development Jack Ellis served as a resource person in charge of financial management. University interior designer William Dombroski supervised the project in cooperation with committee members and a Cincinnati architectural consultant, Harry Backus.

To finance restoration, refurbishing, and preservation of the historic building, the Konnekers pledged a dollar for every two dollars raised from private gifts, up to a total of $300,000. The Office of Alumni Relations and the Alumni Association promoted it as a nationwide challenge, through which areas of the new center could be named for individuals or organizations. This brought a healthy response for sponsorships of hallways, the entryway, dining room, parlor, reception-warming area, library, kitchen, offices, a wraparound veranda, and landscaping. The three-story building also had seven fireplaces and a full basement, part of which was converted into a large conference room. Long before the work was completed, alumni director Adams and his staff moved in, amidst the clutter and clatter of rewiring, replastering, replumbing, refurbishing stairways and floors, and installing air-conditioning.

Ann Lee Konneker and Claire Ping, who shared interests and experience in interior decorating and antiques, shouldered the responsibility for furnishing the twelve-room house. Despite being constructed at the turn of the twentieth century, the house reflected Greek Revival design, the dominant style of American domestic architecture from 1830 to 1850, when its popularity led it to be labeled the national style. The two women, with only temporary, futile opposition from their husbands and the alumni director but strong support from other members of the committee, decided that furnishings of that period were most appropriate for the elegant structure that was listed on the National Register of Historic Places. "We were afraid they would make it into a museum instead of an alumni house," Will said, "but, of course they won, and rightly so."

Working with St. Louis historical consultant Alyce "Sparkle" Mortland, Ann Lee traveled to major cities from New York to San Francisco, Chicago to New Orleans, becoming quite knowledgeable about nineteenth-century furnishings. Meanwhile, Claire and a student of Human and Consumer Sciences Professor Catherine Steiner designed the kitchen area. Dr. Steiner also used the building and its original plans for segments of courses in historic preservation and period furnishings.

Many antiques of the Greek Revival period were difficult to find, so the planning committee sent a wish list and precise descriptions of desired items to alumni and friends. In response, the committee received financial pledges to purchase valuable rugs, chandeliers, tables, lamps, mirrors, and upholstered armchairs, to complete the restoration.

During negotiations for purchasing the building, committee member Rose Rutherford, widow of Dwight H. Rutherford, former president of the alumni association and a charter member of the fund board, purchased the two-story carriage house behind the main edifice. Rose intended to live there, but she died on October 6, 1980. Subsequently, the Konnekers donated enough additional money for the fund to purchase the building from her heirs, and it became a special guesthouse for visiting alumni and friends. Ann Lee and Claire redecorated the small building, assisted by Anne Grover, an antique buff and wife of university trustee B. T. "Tad" Grover Jr., who lived in Athens. They also cooperated in refurbishing a nineteenth-century log cabin, which became the university's Welcome Center, and an Athens home used to accommodate eminent Malaysian scholars who came to Ohio through an endowed chair program.

(The Tun Abdul Razak Chair, established in 1979 and named for Malaysia's second prime minister who had died three years earlier, was supported by funds from that country's government and U.S. firms with business interests in that country. The first foreign endowed chair to be established at a U.S. public university, it was announced at the Washington residence of Malaysian Ambassador Zain Azraai, in a ceremony attended by the ambassador, Ping, Konneker, Ellis, and Ohio Senator John Glenn. Chair holders were to be assigned for two-year terms, teaching and doing research in their chosen fields. Part of the endowment provided also for purchases of library materials, which evolved several years later into part of a major Southeast Asia collection containing well over 110,000 titles.)

To complete their alumni center contributions, Will and Ann Lee established a $1 million endowment for perpetual maintenance of the building and grounds, so it never would become a financial drain on the university. Later, Leona Hughes, a 1930 graduate, member of the foundation board, and longtime major benefactor of the university, established an endowment to supplement the maintenance fund. The renovated building helped Ohio University receive one of three 1981 national awards for exceptional achievement for the total alumni program from the Council for the Advancement and Support of Education. It was dedicated as the W. R. Konneker Alumni Center at the October 10, 1981, homecoming, with a host of visitors attending the ceremony and touring the building. Appropriate period engraved nameplates throughout the house identified restoration donors and furnishings contributors.

The very next month, Will and Ann Lee took part in an elaborate event relating indirectly to their recent university activities and directly to Will's presidency of the Alumni Association. The U.S. Department of State asked President Ping if Ohio University would consider awarding an honorary degree to Tun Hussein Onn, successor to Tun Abdul Razak, who was retiring as prime minister of Malaysia because of ill health. Ohio University had been active for several years in designing and providing business education at Mara Institute, helping prepare Malaysian men and women for leadership roles in their country's expanding commerce. So close was the relationship that Mara graduates also were considered to be Ohio University alumni. Moreover, the popular prime minister, who was well respected throughout the world, and whom President Ping described as "the Jefferson of a newly established nation in terms of significant education," had been prominent in his country's endowment of the Razak chair.

Ping's reply to the State Department was that the university would be pleased and honored to present the honorary degree of Doctor of Laws and Public Service to Tun Hussein Onn. Enthusiastic Malaysian government officials considered it an exceptional opportunity to honor the man widely revered by his countrymen. A spokesperson, in fact, explained that visitors from the Ohio campus would be guests of the Malaysian government and insisted that the university party be large, befitting the occasion. The American State Department showed a similar interest, providing a letter of congratulations from President Ronald Reagan, to be read at a banquet following the ceremony.

In late November 1981, Charles and Claire Ping led an entourage to Kuala Lumpur, capital of the federation of Malaysia. With them were Alumni President Konneker and Ann Lee; Trustee Chairman Elect G. Kenner Bush, publisher of the *Athens Messenger,* and his wife, Margene; and University Vice President Kurlinski and his wife, Virginia.

The five-day chain of events that followed featured limousine processions to view historic sites, visit the king, attend various cultural programs, and prepare for the upcoming presentation. Each visiting couple had a separate limousine and driver, always traveling in the designated order—president, trustee chairman, alumni president, and university vice president. On the next to the last day, the procession advanced along a curving hill, flanked by light poles that had been draped with buntings alternating the colors of Ohio University and Malaysia, to Parliament House, situated near the city's beautiful Lake Gardens. There a protocol committee of about fifty members, headed by a brigadier general, determined procedures and exact seating for the main event. The group returned the next day, following the same route amidst the same decorations to join an academic processional of Ohio University–Mara alumni to the main parliament chamber. During the ensuing two-hour program, President Ping conferred the degree, Lord President Tun Justice Mohamed Suffian Hashim delivered a public oration, and the lord justice of the Supreme Court presented a shorter address. Prime Minister Mahathir bin Mohammad, his deputy, members of the cabinet, and foreign ambassadors also attended the affair described in the November 29, 1981, Malaysia *New Straits Times:*

> It is no ordinary occasion. It is a sterling testimony to the great service rendered by a son of Malaysia to his people and country. It is also a recognition of the Tun as an international statesman who has devoted his life for the betterment of the world. The conferment also signifies the strengthening ties in various fields between Malaysia and the United States. It is thus a recognition of both the former premier and the nation.

A black-tie dinner was held that evening in the House of Parliament's Great Hall, also decorated with the green and white of Ohio University and the red, white, blue, and yellow of Malaysia.

The 1804 Campaign raised $23.6 million, a sizable amount for the early eighties. Equally important in the minds of many, it helped restore a positive campus attitude, as President Ping hoped it would do. Out of it emerged the 1804 Fund, a permanent internal endowment providing more than $500,000 annually for teaching and research initiatives, such as start-up money for faculty/student projects.

During the campaign—at the 1979 homecoming—Will Konneker was named Ohio University "Alumnus of the Year." The following June, he received an honorary Doctor of Laws degree at commencement exercises, and that fall Ann Lee was named Honorary Alumna. In 1982, Will became chairman of the Ohio University Fund Board of Trustees, succeeding Eugene Rinta, of Silver Springs, Maryland, a 1938 graduate who had served in that capacity (although with the title of president) since 1973.

Will almost simultaneously completed his 1804 Campaign chairmanship and his commitment as a half-time consultant to Mallinckrodt. As those responsibilities ebbed, however, others rolled in so rapidly the overall tide of work never receded. For instance, he accepted an invitation to join the Washington University Alumni Board of Governors in 1982, beginning a long tenure in which he would serve two terms as chairman.

Primarily on his initiative, plans were started to establish a Washington University Arts and Sciences graduate fellowship in the name of the late Arthur Hughes, for whom the lecture hall was named in the seventies. During some administrative turnovers, the intended project faded from the high priority list, but not from Will's memory. Meanwhile, a new member of the staff, John "Jack" Pirozzi, was given the assignment of organizing a triple challenge for the College of Arts and Sciences annual fund drive. Pirozzi had come to Washington University from Hiram College in Ohio, where he was dean of admissions and director of foundation resources, to be director of development for the College of Arts and Sciences. He long remembered his first meaningful encounter with Will:

I realized how important the triple challenge assignment was. The idea was to find a parent, an alumnus, and a business that would contribute enough money to create the base for a substantial challenge campaign. Well, I found the parent and an individual alumnus, but being new to the university and the area, I had difficulty identifying an interested business. Arts and sciences is not a big-money arena, and we were getting dangerously close to the end of a fiscal year, at which time we would lose the two pledges. For a recently hired person anxious to make a favorable start, that was nearly a time for panic. So I looked through cards, found Konneker Development, which sounded kind of like a business, and decided to take a flyer. As it turned out, it was the same person who was on the alumni board, but that was only a coincidence at the time. I made an appointment for the first of July, went to see Will, and rather nervously, I'm afraid—thinking that if I failed the effort might fall apart—explained what was needed. I tried not to emphasize the urgency, because I didn't want him to feel we were trying to apply pressure, not yet knowing that pressure has no effect on him. Will sat back in his chair, thought for a while, then said in a quiet voice, "I think that is do-able." That was it. I believe the next day was the best Fourth of July I've ever experienced. I was able to go back and tell the dean we could go into the new fiscal year with a challenge grant in place—our first ever in arts and sciences.

While the drive was under way, Will reminded Jack about a desire to again honor his former professor, Dr. Hughes, by helping establish graduate fellowships in his name. "I am going to put money up front so that you can go out and get more to go with it," he told his new friend. That goal too was achieved at about the time the triple challenge came to a successful climax, with Will helping with the footwork as well as the giving.

Asked why he didn't reserve a little space on his calendar for such things as golf or tennis at that point in his life, the laconic Will Konneker grinned and replied simply, "I flunked retirement."

No matter how involved Will Konneker became in a wide spectrum of business and philanthropic endeavors, he always seemed to find a spare pocket of time when challenged by a new sideline. In 1976, while Will was serving his third year as president of the Ohio University Alumni Association, Keith

Welsh, a 1960 graduate, became director of alumni affairs. Keith's off-duty passion was training and driving racehorses, and he was licensed in both aspects of the sport. Intrigued with discussions on the subject, Will recalled, "The next thing I knew, he and I owned a pacer."

After rather dismal results at county fairs, the horse came up lame, so the two men went to a Tattersall sale at Red Mile Harness Track in Lexington, Kentucky, where Will purchased a Standardbred filly, which they named "WK Girl." This time they "faired" better, and did well also on circuit levels that included such tracks as Scioto Downs in Columbus and Northridge in Cleveland. The partnership continued after Welsh left his position at the university and sold real estate in Athens, but, tragically, he was killed in a train accident on April 13, 1979. After selling the filly, Will used the money to purchase an annuity for his friend's two children.

11

INNOVATIONS IN EDUCATION

*The direction in which education starts a
man will determine his future life.*

—PLATO

Almost as a counterpoint to their activities in the spirited seventies, the Konnekers bought a summer home in the tranquil setting of Chautauqua Lake, New York. The purchase, however, came as a surprise to Will.

Chautauqua Institution, located in the southwestern tip of the state, was founded in 1874 as a Sunday school assembly but had been transformed during the next one hundred years into a world-renowned center for arts, education, religion, and recreation. Beautiful homes, hotels, lecture halls, and youth camps gave the gated community the appearance of a campus community. Cultural and entertainment programs attracted top national talent for summer engagements, creating a fame that nearly overshadowed the purpose for which the institution had been planned. Ann Lee's sister, Jane Edwards, a teacher in the Columbus suburb of Westerville, spent every summer at the institution, staying with their parents when they owned a house there and then renting apartments. Her husband, Maynard, a Columbus attorney, died in a 1953 traffic accident, leaving her with a five-year-old son, Jeffrey. Ann Lee, sometimes accompanied by Will, visited Jane at Chautauqua for a week or two each summer.

In the spring of 1975, Ann Lee drove with her sister to Chautauqua during Jane's spring break to help locate a summer apartment. But a few days later, Ann Lee telephoned her husband to announce the startling news that she would be late returning home because they were snowed in—in mid-April. When she finally returned to St. Louis, she delivered another bombshell. "Guess what," she said, "we own a little summer cottage." Asked for an explanation, she answered with a question: "What else can you do when you're snowed in and you don't ski, except to go around and look at real estate?"

A month later, the couple drove the seven hundred miles to Chautauqua for a good look at their new investment. In Will's words, "The little cottage was a century-old three-story home with plumbing down the outside, because it was only a summer residence." The new owners began renovation of the third floor, which became living quarters for Jane, then worked gradually on the other two levels. In the spring of 1977, however, a plumber's error led to a fire that nearly gutted the top floor and left water damage throughout the rest of the house.

After the restored structure again was repaired, it became known as "The Konneker House," in keeping with a tradition of identifying summer homes by owners' names. With Chautauqua Lake less than a block away, Will bought a Chris-Craft inboard-outboard boat, and they began spending about two or sometimes three summer weeks there, relaxing, attending daily events, and anticipating a time well into the future when they might go for the entire nine-week season, from late June until Labor Day.

By the beginning of the eighties, the close association of President Ping and Dr. Konneker through Alumni Association and Fund affairs, particularly the recent campaign, had fostered an enduring personal friendship between the two families. They enjoyed being together socially and liked to brainstorm prescient visions of the university.

During one such occasion at the Konneker home, after the Pings had attended a St. Louis alumni meeting, the president described his long-held concern for the welfare of southeastern Ohio. "In addition to our responsibility for educating students, conducting research, and being active in community affairs," he told his friend, "we also have an obligation, in my opinion, for economic development in our depressed region of the state." Konneker responded that some of the university's research might be adapted to products and services that could become marketable through outside companies.

The conversation expanded into a discussion of business incubators being tried, with about a 50 percent rate of success in some parts of the country, and whether or not such a program might be appropriate for Appalachian Ohio. No conclusion was reached, but the idea simmered in both men's minds, reappearing frequently in subsequent meetings. Meanwhile, President Ping moved ahead early in 1982 by naming an ad hoc committee of faculty and administrators to investigate the feasibility of developing a research park. Dean of Arts and Sciences William F. Dorrill chaired the group, which, in the words of President Ping, "did a very thorough job."

After visiting facilities in various locations, talking with administrators, studying relevant literature, and discussing the concept in campus meetings, the committee reported that successful research parks depended on having either the luxury of prosperous industries located in their areas or the ability to attract them. For that reason, it recommended that the university establish a centrally located Innovation Center as a first step, then consider acquiring nearby land for development of a research park. It specifically suggested acreage at the State of Ohio's Athens Mental Health Center, where the majority of operations were being phased out. Members also emphasized that the Innovation Center would need to have "a knowledgeable, visible, and involved" director and "a formal organization for administering the authority," which should be "a non-profit type of corporation with a simple, clear, unbureaucratic structure."

During a series of meetings with university administrators who would be most directly involved in such a project, operational guidelines, legal issues, and space requirements were determined. President Ping invited Will to "come and look around and see what you think," then convinced him to start up and direct an Innovation Center at a salary of one dollar per year. Alan H. Geiger, then university planner and later assistant to the president, observed, "Dr. Konneker was widely regarded as the essential ingredient needed for success."

On January 29, 1983, the university's board of trustees formally established the Ohio University Innovation Center and Research Park Authority, naming President Ping as chairman, albeit an ex officio member. This arrangement, board members reasoned, would enable the authority to become an independent agency while preserving involvement by the university. Regular charter members were Dean Dorrill, Engineering and Technology Dean T. Richard Robe, Business Administration Dean John E. Stinson, University Trustee Bush, and Dr. Ralph Schey, a 1948 business graduate, Ohio University Fund trustee, and chief executive officer of the Scott Fetzer Corporation of Cleveland. Although Dr. Konneker was to have direct control of the Innovation Center's development and operations, making decisions rather independently, the authority would vote on proposals he recommended from individuals or groups interested in starting businesses.

At subsequent meetings, the group decided that criteria must include a willingness to pay minimal rent and office expenses, as well as offering some business equity to the center, usually in the form of stock. These terms would be negotiated individually with prospective tenant companies. In this way, the Innovation Center, one of the first of its kind in the nation, would help faculty researchers commercialize their findings, and outside clients could utilize the university's expertise and technical support.

Headquarters for the new Innovation Center provided a warm touch of nostalgia for Director Konneker. Old Morton Hall at One President Street, abandoned in 1979 and mothballed pending eventual replacement, was partially restored instead for at least temporary use. Most often referred to as the zoology building, it nevertheless had housed chemistry classrooms and laboratories when Will was a student. By repairing and painting the first floor of the deserted four-story building and adding new white metal lettering across the front of its brick facade, the university converted an old structure—built in 1910—into a bare-bones harbinger of the future.

Standing outside the building, Will could duplicate the viewpoint but not the view he had from the Delt house in 1943. The fraternity had moved, making way for an engineering building that in turn was being replaced by a new complex on the West Green campus he could see in the distance. He could look down across the same President Street bridge, but the Hocking River was gone. Through an extraordinary effort by the U.S. Army Corps of Engineers, it had been rerouted to bypass the campus and eliminate the recurring floods. As a result, the athletic fields he had viewed four decades earlier now were greatly expanded and surrounded by classrooms, dormitories, and the College of Osteopathic Medicine.

Distant buildings of the mental health facility looked much the same as before. Yet appearance in no way reflected what had taken place. Farming had faded gradually during the sixties, but the coup de grace to all work by patients had been delivered later by a single legal blow. Programs once designed to help improve self-esteem through productive pursuits involving nearly two thousand patients had been forsaken after a federal court ruled in 1972 that persons committed to mental health facilities no longer could work without pay. What remained of agricultural and dairy activities, even upkeep of a part of the grounds, had to be abandoned. Lacking sufficient funds to compensate patients for outside work or finance inside supervision, the hospital administration confined them to small rooms, each with a single, barred window. Three-fourths of them were transferred to other institutions or released to relatives and halfway houses. Patient population dwindled to about three hundred by the mid-seventies, and when it was decided that round-the-clock restriction was cruel, many were permitted to roam the streets of Athens. Most of the more than seventy buildings on the grounds of what recently had been renamed the Athens Mental Health Center were abandoned.

Will Konneker was among many Americans who believed transitions from outdoor work activities to indoor confinement—nationwide, not just in Athens—exemplified irresponsible political pressures, followed by knee-jerk legislation, sparking an unfortunate chain reaction in the growth of homelessness and hopelessness among the mentally ill. He accepted that the movement was irreversible, yet his opinion transcended even the course of events that would link him to the hospital acreage being phased out of operation. The committee that had recommended establishment of an Innovation Center also had suggested that site for its proposed research park, and it was hoped that the Ohio General Assembly would deed much of the 721 acres there to the university. A small portion was being sought by various other organizations in the county, including a group that was leasing the dairy barn from the state and converting it into a community arts center. (Indeed, it was destined to become known nationwide as the Dairy Barn Southeastern Ohio Cultural Arts Center, after receiving a deed from the 116th Ohio General Assembly in 1986.)

The Ohio University Fund provided $50,000 in start-up money, and the Ohio General Assembly made a line-item appropriation of $375,000 for the 1983–85 biennium. Now the immediate challenge was to activate plans for the Innovation Center, an effort that took Will to the campus for two weeks each month. He envisioned programs that would produce new regional companies, expand faculty opportunities, and even provide employment and experience for students. Alan Geiger, continuing his responsibilities as university planner, assumed additional duties as the center's associate director to serve as liaison with the university administration and help with organizational affairs of new companies. He also made arrangements for the renovations, which would be carried out intermittently as projects expanded. Dinah Adkins, who held B.A. and M.A. degrees in English from Ohio University, was hired to direct marketing and public relations. Dinah had been a journalist in Oregon and Virginia before returning to Athens in 1978 as a writer in the Ohio University Office of Public Affairs and a freelancer for newspapers and magazines. Many of her articles dealt with research projects. Jane Griffith, who had a background in accounting and computers, soon joined the administrative group to manage the office, supervise students who worked on part-time jobs, and provide secretarial, bookkeeping, computer, and other business services for new companies. Her previous work with a CPA firm provided her with experience in payrolls and payroll taxes, immediate concerns that would be especially critical for novice enterprises.

With the lack of a strong industrial base in southeastern Ohio, Will had long ago determined that "with so much research going on at the university, we should start by looking at the laboratory areas and see what is brewing." More than a year before the Innovation Center was established officially, he had become fascinated by research of recombinant genetics, commonly known as gene splicing, being conducted by two top university scientists, biochemists Thomas E. Wagner and Joseph Jollick. When they announced the world's first successful transfer of a functioning gene from one species of mammal to another—a rabbit to a mouse—on September 8, 1981, Will was there, along with media representatives from across the country. The following day, a front-page article in the *International Herald Tribune,* published with the *New York Times* and *Washington Post,* reported:

> The achievement is a first that can be expected to speed the progress of genetic engineering—in this case, engineering to transfer some traits of one creature to another, first in animals

but then, very possibly, in man. . . . The scientists first obtained segments of the genetic material, or DNA, that makes up the rabbit gene that produces beta-globin, one of two molecules in rabbit hemoglobin. They then flushed egg cells from the oviducts of female mice just hours after the females mated. They injected the rabbit DNA into these egg cells, directly into the male pronucles—that is, the male mouse sperm that had already entered the female egg cells and begun to swell. That is the first step just before the sperm combine with female genetic material to give future offspring what ordinarily would be a two-parent heritage.

A Nobel Prize–winning scientist announced that what the two men claimed to have accomplished "cannot be done" but later had to admit it had, indeed, been done. Other scientists hailed it as a pivotal achievement.

After attending a seminar conducted by the two teacher/researchers following their heralded announcement, Konneker was convinced their work in several areas of biochemistry could form bases for business partnerships. Coincidentally, a company named Genetic Engineering, formed in New York but set up in Denver, had investigated that possibility even before the official announcement was made.

Lacking microsurgical equipment for their experiments, Wagner and Jollick had obtained collaboration with Peter C. Hoppe of the Jackson Hole Laboratories in Bar Harbor, Maine, who had the apparatus to bridge that gap. "Unfortunately, one of my most important research instruments at that time was the telephone," Wagner recalled later.

The resulting patent for transgenics procedures, in the name of Wagner and Hoppe but assigned to Ohio University, was licensed to Genetic Engineering, which had laboratories and a farm facility where it was dealing with swine. As part of the arrangement, Dr. Wagner was granted a sabbatical leave extending into 1982 to help the company develop its plans for commercialization.

Arriving in Colorado, "ready to roll up my sleeves and go to work," Wagner became disenchanted when he realized "the company's immediate intention was to expound on the potential of the research, use its notoriety to go public, and then liquidate stock for a quick profit." Able to dissolve the relationship but not the exclusive license, he continued the

sabbatical at Cambridge University in England, where he gained expertise in microbiosurgery to augment his research techniques. Meanwhile,
his Ohio University assistant, Dr. Jung Yun, gained similar knowledge by
working with Hoppe at Bar Harbor.

While Wagner was gone, Will posed a question to Dr. Jollick: "Why
couldn't we use some of the things you are doing to identify viruses, or
things of that nature in the medical field?" Receiving a positive reply, he
funded a small laboratory for Jollick to explore such a possibility. Jollick,
an associate professor of microbiology and biomedical sciences, was able to
prove that he could identify strep throat through a technique known as
hybridization, and soon after the Innovation Center opened its doors for
business in the summer of 1983, Molecular Diagnostics became its first
significant client. When it was discovered that a company named Molecular Diagnostics already existed in Connecticut, the fledgling Athens corporation changed to Diagnostic Hybrids, with Will serving as president
and Jollick vice president.

David Scholl, who had worked with Jollick as a young graduate student (and had taken a freshman course in biochemistry from Wagner) remembered the experience as "witnessing a lot of the process high-flying
technology goes through at a university not normally in the high-flying
sector but battling some more prominent research organizations." After
receiving his Ph.D. and spending a year in a postdoctorate program at the
Roche Institute for Molecular Biology in Nutley, New Jersey, Scholl got
an even closer look at the Innovation Center. Encouraged by Jollick, he returned to Athens as director of research for Diagnostic Hybrids. It was a
move both he and Will Konneker would applaud for many years to come.

Progress was slow in a business sense. The company developed tests
that could ascertain strep throat and herpes, using radioactivity as the detecting device, and received FDA approval. But most virologists, being
unfamiliar with radioactivity, were reluctant to use it. "We had a laboratory success but an apparent commercial failure," Konneker said.

Diagnostic Hybrids, Inc., often referred to simply as DHI, remained
marginally solvent, surviving almost entirely on seed money provided
personally by Konneker, stock purchases by the Ohio University Fund,
and research grants rather than sales. To help relieve the pressure, Will
contacted Japanese friends at Daiichi Pure Chemical, a subsidiary of
Daiichi Seiyaku. (He had worked with the parent company to form the

joint-venture Daiichi Radioisotope Laboratories when he was with Mallinckrodt.) Persuading Daiichi Pure Chemical management to invest in the financing of DHI research, he returned to Athens with a pledge of $1 million, which he described as a godsend. Asked if there was any guarantee involved, he replied, "No. You're smart not to make any guarantee on research. If you knew for sure what would take place, it wouldn't be research." Obtaining backing depended on selling ideas and convincing the right people that the organization has the background to make them work, he said, "but you can't promise positive results." The Japanese received everything they requested and were thoroughly satisfied with results of the research, but they didn't follow through on their long-range plans, a situation never fully explained to Will.

DHI tried an assortment of marketing plans, with barely discernable results, yet managed to retain a positive image for innovative research and development of transgenic technology, expanding both its scientific scope and its product lines. "Will always stressed patience and persistence," Scholl said. "He put his time and effort—I call it sweat equity—into it. The magic, he said, is in hard work, and he never gave up on that. So neither did the rest of us."

While Diagnostic Hybrids was struggling, Ohio Gov. Richard F. Celeste began to promote programs of excellence, in keeping with campaign promises to increase the direct role of universities as a dynamic force in overcoming Rust Belt problems of the past and revitalizing the state's economy. One specific proposal, endorsed by the federal government, was to forge a Thomas Alva Edison Partnership Program that could foster cooperative efforts between higher education and business. Funds provided by the state to Edison Centers at universities were to be matched by support from companies in those areas. Ping, Konneker, and Wagner met with the governor several times, explaining the potential that Ohio University's recently recognized achievements in genetic engineering offered.

The governor was aware of the university's leadership in that field but believed its location and limited reputation for research would have to be overcome. Some faculty members had done well in obtaining individual backing—Wagner himself had received annual grants from the National Institutes of Health since joining the faculty in 1970—but for the millions of dollars involved in an Edison Partnership, the university lacked a critical mass, meaning the ability to form strengths by focusing groups of experienced researchers and facilities on auspicious projects. Unfortunately, there was no nearby major research facility, such as a Cleveland Clinic, to bridge the gap.

That limitation, plus the absence of corporations capable of hefty financing, were pointed out by the governor. However, he was receptive to a suggestion that Konneker and Wagner form a company that could be built into the business partner needed to qualify for such a program. They had, in fact, already been planning just such a company based on the technology of genetically altering farm animals to improve yields of meat from hogs. Because of this, a special arrangement might be possible to set up an Edison Center at the university and license its technological findings exclusively to the new company, which would then generate matching funds. Wagner was given the assignment of preparing an application, which became the size of a large city telephone book when it was finished in the early fall of 1982 and submitted the following January. When the state legislature accepted Governor Celeste's plan a year later, Ohio University was one of six initial Edison Technology Centers partially funded through the Department of Development. Dr. Wagner was appointed director. An outside board of directors, made up of advisers from statewide businesses, was appointed to meet twice a year to offer perspectives on scientific projects and maintain a close relationship with the sponsoring government agencies. Many of its members proved to be very helpful through the years ahead.

Started by three persons in a small Irvine Hall laboratory on the West Campus, the Edison Animal Biotechnology Center (EABC) focused at first on the production of transgenic animals, pioneered by the research team Wagner headed. By that time, Genetic Engineering in Denver had given up thoughts of utilizing the original patent licensing from Ohio University and agreed to sell it back, enabling Konneker and Wagner to form the partnership company Embryogen, headquartered at the Innovation Center. Konneker, who had provided initial funding, with his typical specification that his share of any profits would go to the university, became president and CEO. Wagner was named vice president, with John F. Burns, director of university legal affairs, serving as secretary-treasurer.

With the Edison arrangement in place, Embryogen contracted to use a farm and livestock owned by the Lackey family of nearby Stewart, Ohio, to advance its experimental endeavors, while the two founders set out to raise private capital. "I was on the road again, this time with Tom Wagner," Will said. They quickly received $500,000 from Nationwide Insurance Company of Columbus, a logical source in view of its ownership by the Ohio Farm Bureau. But the state's initial funding of the Edison Center was $3.1 million, which had to be matched, along with all future grants.

Although Konneker had been among those instrumentally involved in obtaining the Edison program, he stressed the Innovation Center's independent status in a by-lined article, "The Challenge of turning research into jobs for Ohio," distributed by a statewide news service in October of 1985:

> Universities have to recognize that research whose goal is commercialization is different from research whose goal is the advancement of knowledge. Where one must be kept secret, the other must be left open to the public. Accordingly, we have designed the Innovation Center so that faculty members and others working to turn ideas into commercial products can perform their work in a setting that is physically separate and offers all necessary proprietary protection. . . . Basic research must be allowed to continue. It continues to be a prime source for intellectual vitality that is the essence of any good academic institution. Individual researchers must come under no pressure to abandon areas of basic inquiry.

Renovations continued at the Innovation Center as the number of businesses grew slowly. Fortunately many laboratory facilities remained from the Old Morton Hall era, although some plumbing had been ripped from the walls. Soon, all four floors were ready for use, either by start-up groups or as temporary spill-over areas for university departments. Dinah Adkins succeeded Alan Geiger as associate director of the center in 1986, Jane Griffith became director of business affairs, and Will concentrated on working with individual companies located there.

On May 5, 1988, the Innovation Center observed its fifth anniversary and National Small Business Week with an open house and reception. Visitors toured the facility at One President Street, examining products and discussing prospects for ten business occupants, including Diagnostic Hybrids and Embryogen. Among the others:

• Athens Technical Specialists, Inc., founded and owned by Dr.

James C. Gilfert, who had taken early retirement in 1983 to develop an automatic tester for traffic signal conflict voltage monitors, which are responsible for safe operation of traffic signals. Based on expertise he gained through research in electrical engineering, Gilfert started his company in the basement of his home before he became the first anchor tenant of the Innovation Center—a reference to companies started elsewhere but moving to the center. After it gained endorsement of the Ohio Division of Transportation, the product became in great demand by municipalities, counties, states, and private service contractors throughout the United States, Canada, and Puerto Rico. Satisfied customers even sent him suggestions for other testing equipment that might be needed, further fueling his expansion activities.

- Golden Soy Foods, Inc., producer of tofu-based food products sold to conventional groceries, regional cooperatives, and health foods marketers throughout the United States and Canada.

- Auto Automation, Inc., developer of blast-hole logging equipment and coal mine design software.

- Specialized Timers, Inc., which developed and marketed timing products for heavy-duty industrial uses.

- Other products reflecting a diversity of interests, ranging from tie-dyed clothing and musical folk instruments to motion pictures.

Electronic Visions, Inc., an early tenant and recent "graduate" of the center, relocated to its own building—a move representing a goal of business incubation. It was founded by former students David Burke and Dan Krivicich, who spent nine months developing interactive videodisc technology before obtaining a series of contracts that sent sales and employment soaring.

The experience Dinah Adkins gained at the Innovation Center enabled her to become part-time executive director of the fledgling National Business Incubation Association, which was founded in Pennsylvania by a group of industrial leaders in 1985. In 1989, she became its full-time chief staff executive, and the association moved its headquarters to Athens as a second anchor tenant of the center. Nine years later, with a greatly expanded staff, regular groups of student interns, and a membership growing from forty to nearly eight hundred, she was named president and CEO.

Several changes took place in the state's Edison funding and at EABC in the late eighties and early nineties. Instead of grants being issued directly to participants, total funding went to BioTechnology Center, Inc., in Cleveland, which in turn made financial distributions to affiliates. The Ohio University group, which had moved from its original laboratory into a larger facility in one section of Wilson Hall, a West Green dormitory, maintained its operational autonomy. But it officially became a center of excellence in the new network.

Dr. John J. Kopchick, known nationally for his studies of growth hormone genes and molecular biology, joined the Ohio University faculty in 1987 as a Goll-Ohio Eminent Scholar and quickly became an undisputed leader in EABC research. To provide an endowment that would lure Kopchick from Merck Sharp and Dohme Research Laboratories of Rahway, New Jersey, the university obtained $500,000 from a 1935 alumnus, Milton Goll, an industrial microbiologist and founder of Cosan Chemical Corporation, to match a similar amount from the state of Ohio. In addition to his research and an impressive series of patented inventions, Kopchick became an adviser to many successful Ph.D. and master's degree candidates.

During the second round of grant requests for Edison Centers, an unidentified person at the state level questioned the advisability of Tom Wagner continuing to direct EABC while playing a key leadership role in its sole beneficiary, Embryogen, and holding the faculty rank of full professor. No accusation was implied; the concern was the *appearance* of an actual conflict of interests. It was suggested, however, that separation beyond an arms-length association would be politically advisable. Negotiations were, in fact, proposed as a requisite for further funding.

After considering several alternatives, all parties agreed that the most feasible solution was to appoint a nonscientific EABC director with business experience but no financial interest in Embryogen. The man they selected was John Jarvis, a former St. Louis business associate of Will, who had come from industry to join DHI two years earlier. Wagner was given the title of scientific director, enabling him to work, particularly in tandem with John Kopchick, without being responsible for administrative matters. In the years ahead, EABC would broaden its basic and applied research programs, maintaining a steady growth pattern funded by the university, the Department of Development, federal and private grants, corporate research contracts, royalties, and licensing fees.

Embryogen was continuing to progress, but after the success with Nationwide Insurance, the problem of obtaining further financial backing had become surprisingly difficult. Knocking on corporate and venture capitalist doors blanketing the state proved to be unproductive. Agricultural products afforded no appeal to investors looking for large margins of profit. Extending their quest beyond state boundaries, Konneker and Wagner encountered similar adversity, until they located an interested group of East Coast venture capitalists, the principal one headquartered in Princeton, New Jersey. Matching money would be forthcoming, they were assured, with one condition. Embryogen would have to be combined with another company the consortium had funded earlier, Transgenics, run by scientists associated with Princeton University. Rather than merge, both companies would be required to drop their previous identities and operate as a new corporation called DNX. In return, the Athens segment would receive enough money to meet its matching obligation to the Edison partnership. With no alternative in sight, Embryogen complied.

Emphasis gradually shifted from improving domestic livestock through genetic engineering to the development of swine that would produce human hemoglobin, thereby generating human red cells as an alternative source of blood supplies. It also made headway toward transplanting pigs' livers into humans.

At one meeting of the board, Tom Wagner entered the room, approached Will, who was presiding, and whispered in his ear. Would it be possible, he asked, to fly three small pigs to Duke University in an Ohio University airplane? The animals were being kept in a closely controlled sterile environment and were totally free of exposure to human diseases. There was a good possibility they now could be used to save the life of a man awaiting a liver transplant at the Duke Hospital, if they could be sent out immediately, Tom explained. Without hesitation, Will ended the meeting and emergency arrangements were made to transport the young swine in dog crates to Durham, North Carolina, where their livers were used to keep the man alive for the three days needed to receive his implant. Each of the livers, surgically attached but kept outside his body, could last only one day, but the combination was enough to accomplish the mission. After receiving his human implant, the patient recovered to resume a normal life.

Although the bulk of research activity continued to be carried out for a time in Athens, DNX soon moved management authority to New Jersey. Konneker no longer was president, but he remained on the board of directors to protect equity for the Innovation Center and, ultimately, the university. Exclusive rights to EABC technology were discontinued when Embryogen was dissolved.

DNX abandoned operations at the Lackey farm and built new facilities near Albany, Ohio. Later, it went public, eventually selling part of its operations to Nextran, a Princeton research-oriented firm, and the remainder to Baxter Healthcare Corporation of Deerfield, Illinois, which already had a program involving blood substitutes. Baxter in turn sold its share to the Canadian company Chrysalis, which continued to pay royalty fractions to Ohio University, Thomas Wagner, and Peter Hoppe.

(Wagner, who left Ohio University in 1998 to become director of the Oncology Research Institute in Greenville, South Carolina's Hospital System, remained proud of the role Embryogen played in furthering the university's reputation, and offered a reminder that the Lackey farm "was the progenitor of the animals that someday will be the ones used for organ transplants.")

Since accepting President Ping's request to organize the Innovation Center, Will Konneker had been motivated by a desire to maximize the value of research technologies by getting them into the marketplace, where they could benefit the university, the region, and persons involved in their development. In one sense, this concept was an outgrowth of the idea he had transformed into the creation of his own company in 1950. Applying it to higher education seemed contentious for many years at the majority of universities, where it seemed traditional to have a fear of becoming tainted by involvement with business, industry, or commerce in any form. In actuality, a handful of the nation's most prestigious research universities had been arranging such technology transfers reasonably and quite properly for many years. Nevertheless, like university-affiliated business incubation, it had not become widespread in academic America.

One cornerstone of support for change occurred on December 12, 1980, when the U.S. Congress passed the Bayh-Dole Act, creating a uniform patent policy among the many federal agencies that fund research. The act and several amendments encouraged the assignment of federal grants to faculty and other research investigators, with the express intent of getting patents and marketing their inventions. Prior to the act sponsored by Senators Birch Bayh and Robert Dole, hundreds of patents were left unused because companies in the private sector could not obtain licenses from most federal agencies (even though the latter, who had funded the research, were unable to develop and market inventions themselves), and the few agencies willing to grant patent titles to universities were overwhelmed by obscure and conflicting regulations. Consequently, industrial companies were disinclined to battle bureaucracies in attempts to obtain licenses from government agencies or through universities. Passage of the act removed that barrier, spurring universities to find the means of transferring technology directly from laboratories to the marketplace.

Ohio's Edison program was one of several following the federal example that gradually would change attitudes of dissent among universities where outdated policies might be choking off substantial sources of revenue. Moreover, the acceleration of technology itself in the computer age heralded an obvious need to shorten connectors between universities and the commercial world. Licensing was the most attainable method of marketing university "intellectual properties," although Ohio University's pioneering Innovation Center was proving to be another.

After evolving informally during the last half of the eighties, a Technical Transfer Office was created officially in 1991. Dr. David N. Allen, former member of the Pennsylvania State University faculty and author of the book *Nurturing Advanced Technology Enterprises,* was hired as director of the new office, charged with analyzing research disclosures and determining which merited consideration for pursuing patents. At the same time, he succeeded Dr. Konneker as director of the Innovation Center, and the following year he was given the additional assignment of Edison Center director when John Jarvis left to resume his industrial career. As head of all three groups, Allen was named assistant vice president for technology and economic development.

A succession of administrative changes took place during the remainder of the decade, as all three operational units with which Konneker was associated continued to grow. Linda J. Clark, an Ohio University graduate who had held several financial and informational positions there and in the private sector, moved from managing computer operations in the College of Osteopathic Medicine to handling budgetary matters and assisting Allen in other ways at the Innovation Center and Technology Transfer Office. Robert S. Malott, also an alumnus and associate director of EABC since its inception, became increasingly involved in technology transfers. Before joining the university he had earned a master's degree with distinction from the American Graduate School of International Management and gained several years' corporate experience.

"The major thrust in technology transfers was to provide additional incentive for inventors," Malott said. "That is consistent with the American view of economics. Persons with the largest stakes are going to work hard to see things succeed, and they should be rewarded. Our objective was to reward them and their departments and their colleges, but from the view of equity, share with the university at large so others could benefit from it too." Legal Affairs Director John Burns, who was intensely involved in all such transactions, credited Konneker with initiating the program at Ohio University. "From the time he became director of the Innovation Center, Will was concerned with tech transfer, not as a title, but as a necessary function," Burns said. "The title, in fact, hadn't even entered terminology vocabularies of the academic world, but it certainly was part of the role he was playing. Embryogen and others were good examples." Years later, Will Konneker would help his other alma mater, Washington University of St. Louis, bring its intellectual properties policies up to date.

In May 1988, Ohio's general assembly deeded 670 acres and several buildings of the mental health complex to the university, although thirty of the acres and the main administration building could not be transferred until a new facility was constructed near the city's O'Bleness Memorial Hospital. When that took place in 1991, enabling the university to develop the area, fifty-seven acres became known as "The Ridges," with its centerpiece the Kennedy Museum of Art. Renovation of surrounding structures soon was to convert the property into an integral extension of the university campus. The Innovation Center and the Technology Transfer Office were moved to one of the remodeled buildings in 1994, leaving Diagnostic Hybrids the lone tenant at the main campus facility, which was renamed the

President Street Academic Center. The Edison Center remained in its West Green location, but plans were being formulated to renovate another of the former hospital buildings for its use in the near future.

The statewide change in Edison funding that had established Edison Animal Biology Center as a designated Center of Excellence, loosely affiliated with Edison Biotechnology Centers in Cleveland and other parts of Ohio, created a notable measure of political confusion in names. "The state has these centers here and there and everywhere with none seemingly in the middle," lamented one media reporter. Furthermore, the "A" for "Animal" in EABC had become increasingly extraneous as the emphasis tilted away from agriculture toward biomedical applications. Whatever the reasons—and they varied from source to source—EABC was renamed Edison Biotechnology Institute, with the name most often shortened to EBI.

Will Konneker was appointed to Ohio University's College of Arts and Sciences Board of Visitors in 1986, and two years later he received the college's Achievement Award, based on career accomplishments.

12

BAROMETERS OF FULFILLMENT

Great ability develops and reveals itself increasingly with every new assignment.

—BALTASAR GRACIAN

After B. Lynn Konneker returned home from England in 1986, she worked for a time with Sue Winter in her father's office before accepting successive positions with Trend Décor, a cabinet manufacturing company, and J. L. Johnson Homes, a builder of large home subdivisions in the St. Louis area. She rode other people's horses for a while, but with aspirations to enter show competitions as she had done in England, she soon purchased a Thoroughbred. While she was working with J. L. Johnson, she was introduced by a friend to William H. Webster Jr., who had graduated from Trinity University in San Antonio, Texas, and was employed by St. Louis aircraft manufacturer McDonnell Douglas Corporation, creating training and marketing programs in the Media Department.

Like B. Lynn, Bill Webster was a high school graduate of Principia, although the two had not known each other at that time. They shared experiences with horses, albeit different breeds. As a child in St. Louis, Bill often had gone with his grandfather to a farm the Websters owned near Fulton, Missouri, to ride. During summers, he had been in charge of riding programs at a camp in Colorado, and for a short time he raised quarter horses. More recently he preferred Western riding. His father, a nationally known Missouri lawyer and judge, was best recognized as director of the Federal Bureau of Investigation during the administration of President Jimmy Carter and as head of the Central Intelligence Agency under President Ronald Reagan. Young Bill, however, never lived in Washington, D.C., because he was studying journalism and filmmaking at Trinity during his father's service in the nation's capital. William Sr. had earned his law degree from Washington University in 1949, a year before Will received his Ph.D.

B. Lynn and Bill were married on December 10, 1988, at Graham Chapel, located in the center of the Washington University campus, with Ohio University President Ping, an ordained minister, performing the ceremony. A large group of relatives and friends attending the wedding reflected a wide spectrum of interests impacting the lives of both families.

The young newlyweds moved into a house in the small city of Eureka, a suburb best known as the site of the St. Louis theme park Six Flags. An adjacent barn and pasture were ideally suited for taking care of their horses, and both became members of the Meramec Valley Hunt, one of well over a hundred foxhunting clubs in the United States. The North American sport of mounted riders tracking foxes with packs of hounds differs from the British version in emphasizing the chase, rather than the kill. A successful hunt usually ends with the fox safely entering a hole in the ground and hounds being rewarded simply with praise from riders. The most important aspect is the exhilaration of riding spirited horses through picturesque terrain and over a variety of creeks, walls, and fences, accompanied by the echoing sound of a hunting horn. It is highly organized into membership responsibilities based on experience and skill. B. Lynn and Bill became honorary whips, riding on the flanks of the group to prevent hounds from running onto areas not open to hunting, then worked their way up in the organization to checking the fitness of horses, making certain that landowners' property was not damaged and all gates were closed, building jumps, and in other ways assisting the designated head huntsman. Each hunt was registered with the Masters of Foxhounds Association, assuring that it would meet rigid standards of sportsmanship and animal care. Gaining permission from farmland owners to conduct hunts sometimes could be a problem, but it was attainable because they were scheduled for dates in the late fall, after crops had been harvested, and in the spring, preceding the planting season.

Such outside activities were cut back but not curtailed in 1989 after the couple had a daughter, whom they named Cara. Two years later, William H. Webster III, who would become known as "Trey," was born. "Our lives obviously took on new perspectives," B. Lynn said, "but we were able to continue our hobby, thanks to a fabulous babysitter who would let the children stay with her when necessary." They took care of their own horses, rode them on the property next to their home and at Meramec events, and hauled them to some seasonal opening and closing hunts at clubs in other cities. The family remained at Eureka until Cara was accepted to enter kindergarten at a highly regarded private elementary school, Rossman, in West County, an hour's drive from their home. After searching several areas that would be closer to the school, they purchased the house in Town and Country. In addition to its proximity to the school, the new house was only half a mile from a 100-acre field, which they hoped could be a place to keep their horses. By perusing records, B. Lynn discovered that it was owned by members of the McDonnell family, who permitted them to put their horses there as long as they would take care of the animals and the property, a most fortunate arrangement, indeed.

As the children grew, however, B. Lynn essentially gave up riding. "I was the type of person who set goals, and reaching another one with horses would require serious riding, which means every day," she said. "That couldn't fit in with the much more important one of being a full-time mom, taking care of a house, and doing volunteer work." The latter included participation in the Junior League of St. Louis, the Arts and Education Council, chairing major events of parents clubs, and crusading (successfully) to shut down a Missouri slaughterhouse that killed horses for meat sent to France.

Both Will and Ann Lee had been long-time patrons of arts in St. Louis, at Washington and Ohio Universities, at Chautauqua, and elsewhere. Prompted primarily by a growing friendship and great respect for Dr. Henry H. Lin, dean of Ohio University's College of Fine Arts, they had funded a collection of significant prints for the Trisolini Gallery, first on permanent loan, then as an outright gift. Dr. Lin had suggested that the collection was needed to help enrich gallery exhibits and for a new program bringing together noted outside printmakers, those on the faculty, and students. In St. Louis, the couple attended art exhibits and performances regularly and contributed generously—often anonymously—to fund drives. In the mid-eighties, with his consulting commitment to Mallinckrodt completed, Will became even more personally involved with the arts, principally through long-term board memberships.

One of the first to draw his dedicated participation was the Opera Theatre of St. Louis, which mixed familiar and unconventional repertory performed in English. Of particular interest to Will was the group's policy of showcasing young American singers taught by well-known coaches and directors. Joining the board a few years after the theater was founded in 1976, he was intrigued by this specialization in developing young singers. "We start them in ensembles, give them lessons and scholarships," he said, "and we also bring in those who want to be stage managers, costumers, lighting technicians, and such." Ticket sales brought in less than 30 percent of costs, with the remainder dependent on donations, grants, and eventually an endowment fund. Yet during the next quarter century, the Opera Theatre would never operate in the red—an incredible achievement compared with others across the country—and Will was to continue his board membership during that entire time.

Four operas were performed each year in a garden theater on the campus of Webster University. Within a decade after its opening, it was drawing worldwide attention. In 1983 it became the first U.S. opera company to appear at the Edinburgh International Festival. Its premiere of *Joruri* in Tokyo was the first production of a Japanese opera in Japan by any American company, and it was featured in the first-ever joint BBC/WNET telecast of Albert Herring. The *London Times* referred to the company as "magic on the Mississippi," and its five-week festival season regularly was reviewed in that paper, as well as leading publications in St. Louis, New York, and Chicago. The most important barometers of its success in Will's opinion, however, were its year-round education programs and the growing numbers of young singers that moved on to performing with the Metropolitan Opera. Will became a member of the board's executive committee, which administered most decision making, and the investment committee, overseeing the endowment.

Will attributed a large measure of credit for the Opera Theatre's success to Lawrence Browning, senior vice president and board member of

Emerson Electric Company. A charter member of the Opera Theatre board, "Larry" was one of the persons responsible for its start-up and making certain it operated as a business as well as an art forum. He and his wife, Virginia ("Jinny"), became close friends of Will and Ann Lee as a result of the opera board connection and made periodic overseas trips together.

Selected members of the Saint Louis Symphony Orchestra provided accompaniment for Opera Theatre performances. That association, combined with the Konnekers' enjoyment of symphonic music and some arm-twisting by the director, whom they got to know when they traveled with the group on a concert tour to Hong Kong and China, led to Will's accepting membership, then becoming treasurer and a member of the executive and investment committees of the orchestra's board. Recognized as one of the nation's outstanding symphonies, with a hundred paid musicians on fifty-two-week salaries, it, too, had to look well beyond ticket sales for funding. Powell Symphony Hall, the symphony's home since 1968, was described by violinist Isaac Stern, following a performance there, as ranking with Carnegie Hall in New York and Symphony Hall in Boston.

Yet the city's best-known fine arts building was the Sheldon Concert Hall and Ballroom, designed by the noted 1904 World's Fair architect, Louis C. Spiering, and credited with having perfect acoustics. Speakers at the hall included Albert Einstein, President Dwight D. Eisenhower, and Ernest Hemingway. Some of the world's finest musicians performed in classical, jazz, and chamber music concerts. The Sheldon also hosted post-concert receptions, educational programs for school groups, workshops, masters classes, and a variety of exhibits ranging from architecture and jazz history to children's art. With such an appeal, it was not surprising that Will was persuaded to join the Sheldon board and become active in its proceedings. Several years later, he was elected chairman.

When asked why her husband accepted so many time-consuming responsibilities, Ann Lee explained, "Because people ask him to do it." Yet she became active in similar endeavors, such as the board of the Center of Contemporary Arts (COCA), founded in 1986 to foster appreciation of the arts by producing and presenting performances, exhibitions, and educational programs for students. Its staff grew quickly to ten department heads and a hundred artist-instructors at a center in University City, teaching music, dance, and other arts to students, many of them inner-city children.

Close friends in a circle that expanded with each pursuit came to realize the common thread of motivation really was an educational factor the Konnekers considered essential to the advancement of society. "Most of the problems of the world would be solved with education," Will said. "And there absolutely is only one solution to the inner-city problems, and that is education. Of course, people there need jobs and homes, and other things, but those will only come through education. I feel very strongly about that, and my wife shares that feeling. We make all charitable decisions together."

Philanthropy to him meant devoting thought and energy, as well as money, to this crucial effort. He often considered heeding advice to cut back on his volunteer schedule, but each project seemed important, and the list grew. Secretary Sue Winter provided an insider's view:

> Dr. K is a high-energy person. He is always on the go. His calendar always is full. We go over it every morning when he is in town to make certain of all the things he has to do. He doesn't play golf or anything like that, although he and Ann Lee do like to relax in their pool once in a while. I don't really think he has what you could describe as a normal day. He is in and out of the office a lot. I know he can get aggravated, but it never shows in the office, and it doesn't put him in a bad mood. He always can keep his calm. He has conference calls quite often with different groups, because he is a very active board member, serving on committees, making personal solicitations and things like that. Somehow he can handle a lot of matters at once. Everything he is involved in means giving away his time and money. I consider him an excellent person to have money, because he does a lot of good with it.

In the late eighties, Ohio University President Ping appointed a sixteen-member "Colloquium on the Third Century" to evaluate projected issues and choices that would influence the university's future. As chairman of the Ohio University Fund, Will Konneker was a member of the group, which included representatives of the administration, faculty, and trustees.

Following more than two years of meetings and discussions, an extensive report covering undergraduate, graduate, and professional education, scholarly research, and public service was presented as a sequel to a similar plan covering 1977–87. Adopted by the board of trustees on January 30, 1988, the colloquium report, while making specific suggestions for academic pursuits, emphasized the need for "continuing analysis and reform of undergraduate education, and, at the same time, the strengthening of graduate education and research," both being "essential to the future of the university." The published report did not define the role of the Ohio University Fund, but it accented a dependence on vigorously pursuing financial support from "sources other than the state subsidy." The challenge was clear, albeit between the lines.

Soon after the colloquium finished its mission, Konneker completed a five-year term as Ohio University Fund chairman but remained a member of the thirty-three-year-old organization. He was succeeded by former vice chairman Alan E. Riedel, senior vice president administration (later vice chairman) of Cooper Industries, headquartered in Houston, Texas. Riedel, a 1952 graduate, and his wife, Ruby, who was graduated in 1953, had been active in alumni affairs at local and national levels for many years. Alan had served on the alumni board and raised money in Texas for the 1804 Campaign.

At Riedel's suggestion, trustees of the fund, at their July 1988 meeting, changed its name to the Ohio University Foundation, reasoning that the time had arrived to clarify its autonomous structure, providing more flexibility in raising and distributing funds. "In most persons' minds, a fund implies a source of money for a specified use, whereas a foundation collects and invests money for various purposes over a long period of time," Will reasoned. "Foundation was much more definitive for what we had come to represent." The change also eliminated a confusion created by the continuing 1804 Fund, a singular endowment supporting faculty projects and programs.

Successful fund-raisers believe that one good drive deserves another. Having completed its first-ever capital gifts campaign in the early eighties, however, the university might have seemed susceptible to failure if it tried a second in the same decade. No one was sure, but the Ping administration wanted to keep the momentum, if possible, to have an extraordinary new endowment in place before the end of the century. After

talking with the trustee and foundation boards and receiving favorable re-
sponses, the president hired a professional consultant to survey prominent
alumni and recommend a reasonable goal for another fund drive. The ver-
dict: With an improved information system and proven prospects for
building a richer research base, the university might be able to raise as
much as $65 million. Several members of the optimistic foundation board
insisted that wasn't enough, so, in the words of Chairman Riedel, "We
crossed our fingers and made our goal $100 million."

As a first step in organizing what would be called the Ohio University
Third Century Campaign, foundation trustees searched among themselves
for a campaign chairman. "Most of us felt unable to devote the time and
effort necessary for such a responsibility," Riedel said, "so Will, bless him,
agreed to assume a leadership role, even though he recently had been
through it with the other drive." Will stipulated that he would accept only
if it were a co-chairmanship with another member of the group. Robert P.
Axline Jr. agreed to fill that position.

A 1957 graduate of the university, Bob Axline was president of FIMA
USA, Inc. (later, founder, chairman, and CEO of Plastic Card Systems, Inc.,
in Northboro, Massachusetts). He, too, had a long history of service to the
university through alumni leadership on the East Coast and with the National Alumni Association, membership on various national committees,
and as 1987 executive-in-residence in the College of Business Administration. He and Will were joined by Riedel and Dr. Steven Fuller on a launching committee for the upcoming campaign. Dr. Fuller, a 1941 graduate,
recently had become chairman and CEO of World Book, Inc., Chicago,
after holding an endowed faculty chair at Harvard Business School and a
vice presidency of General Motors Corporation. During several months of
planning, the dauntless foursome kept a chart with a projected line moving ever forward beyond the $100-million goal. Reportedly, that was some-
what disquieting to Vice President Ellis, again serving as campaign
executive director, but he took to his task—and to the road—with enthusiasm and his experienced companion, Will Konneker.

The Third Century Campaign was more organized than its predeces-
sor. Heeding advice of the consultant, Ellis upgraded the development
office in quality and computerized equipment to what Konneker called "a
first-class operation that can be kept intact and built on in the future."
Thirteen regional campaigns blanketed the country. Each had its own

chairman, and Donald H. Voelker, a 1952 graduate, retired president of D. H. Voelker and Associates of Belleair, Florida, and member of the foundation board, was overall chairman of the regional drives. John C. Baker, former university president; Beth K. Stocker, president of the Stocker Foundation; and Edwin L. Kennedy, retired senior partner of Lehman Brothers, were named honorary chairs but served actively on the campaign steering committee.

"It would be impossible to cite all the volunteers who contributed to the campaign's success," Konneker told Nancy Roe, editor of Office of Development publications, near the end of the campaign in the fall of 1993. "The total would reach into the thousands. The money raised is important, of course, but the lasting advantage is that we started the campaign with annual giving of between five and six million dollars, and now it is twelve million. The number of people who give on an annual basis has more than doubled. That's the real benefit."

Axline estimated that the six years of planning and fund-raising took him to the campus several times a year. Konneker was there even more often, but many of his trips included his responsibilities at the Innovation Center. Results of a campaign among faculty and staff members, headed by Dr. Eric Wagner, professor of sociology, again were far beyond expectations, and all members of the foundation board were major donors. Nancy Roe wrote that both co-chairmen paid tribute to their wives, Ann Lee Konneker and Jean Axline, for outstanding support, and quoted Will on crediting Charlie and Claire Ping, who made innumerable trips on behalf of the campaign: "Major donors want to make sure the leadership of the university is fully behind the campaign; that really is a key."

Although an October 1993 black-tie gala at the Convocation Center celebrated its success, the five-year campaign was concluded officially at the end of the year. The final figure of $132 million was hailed by Professor Wagner as creating "an endowment for OU that is one of the largest in the United States." Will Konneker had suggested that he might unwind much of his volunteer effort soon, but at the celebration dinner President Ping hinted strongly that a landmark scholarship program being planned with his friend from St. Louis would be initiated in the near future.

On September 11, 1991, while the Third Century campaign was in progress, Ohio Gov. George V. Voinovich appointed Will Konneker to a nine-year term on the Ohio University Board of Trustees. Konneker considered it a high honor and pledged his best effort to the position when he attended his first meeting in October. Within a few months, however, a small group of Athens-area activists and students, prompted primarily by a blistering attack in a publication named *The Independent*, initiated a drive to have the appointment nullified.

Accusations in the article were reflected in a Student Senate petition to the State Ethics Committee, asking for an investigation of Konneker having possible conflicts of interest because he was on the board of DNX and president of Diagnostic Hybrids. There was no mention of his having supplied original financing for both companies and having pledged all his stock holdings, in writing, to the Ohio University Foundation. To make certain there could be no mistake in carrying out that pledge, he had added a codicil to his will (with a copy to the foundation) assuring that the transfer would take place even if something should happen to him.

Accusations proved to be baseless, but constant pressure, which soon included the fact that Konneker was not a resident of Ohio, was believed by some to prompt a referral of the matter to Atty. Gen. Lee Fisher, a highly respected Cleveland lawyer who had served as a state representative and state senator before being appointed to his new position by Governor Voinovich. After admittedly anguishing over a decision, Fisher ruled that Ohio's constitution clearly limited membership on state boards and commissions to electors, interpreted to be persons eligible to vote in Ohio elections. The decision negated the appointment of Konneker and several persons serving as trustees of other state-assisted universities.

On June 23, 1992, Will submitted a letter of resignation, which was accepted "with regret" by Governor Voinovich, a 1958 graduate of Ohio University. "Will's time in that office might have been the shortest on record," quipped Ann Lee, who, in reality, shared his disappointment.

Although timing of the attorney general's decision indicated to some persons that it was a direct result of opposition from Athens dissenters, university attorney John Burns discounted that influence. "It was something that had been brewing for a long time and had nothing to do with the article panning Will," he said. "Someone in state government finally brought it to the forefront, and the attorney general had to make a ruling. Trustees from other state universities met the same fate."

Two months later, the governor appointed Cleveland attorney Charles

E. Emrick Jr. to complete the eight years remaining on Will's intended term. A 1952 Ohio University graduate and a member of the foundation board, Emrick was serving as northeastern Ohio regional director of the Third Century Campaign. Howard Nolan, a 1957 graduate and head of a major architectural firm in Columbus, became a trustee at the same time, replacing Columbus developer Dennis B. Hefferman, a 1966 graduate whose term had expired.

While the limitation of trusteeships to current citizens of the state seemed outdated and certainly detrimental in many instances, no one questioned the attorney general's interpretation. Some interested groups and individuals made minimal attempts to broach the subject, but the only logical solution appeared to be an amendment to the state constitution— something the general public might consider overkill. To those involved, however, universities were being deprived of dedicated, highly qualified leaders whose careers took them out of the state. Ohio University alone could point to several persons, including investment banker Edwin L. Kennedy of New Jersey, who served illustrious full terms without realizing they were constitutionally unqualified for the positions.

Typically, Konneker displayed no rancor against the protesting students, or even writers of the tabloid article. His letter to Governor Voinovich echoed that feeling: "I am sorry that I will not be able to serve the University as a trustee. However, there are numerous other ways I can and will continue to serve."

Coincidentally, shortly after Konneker's resignation from the Ohio board, he was elected to a four-year term on the Washington University Board of Trustees. Under the leadership of Chancellor William Danforth, grandson of the founder of Ralston-Purina, the private university was growing rapidly in size and acceptance as one of the nation's top research institutions. Its $650 million fund-raising campaign in the mid-eighties was at that time the most successful in the history of higher education. Dr. Danforth, a cardiologist as well as an educator, also served as chairman of the Danforth Foundation, noted for supporting an array of enrichment projects inside and outside American classrooms. Will had numbered the chancellor among his friends since serving two terms as chairman of the Alumni Board of Governors and therefore representing that group as a university trustee.

In addition, since 1986 Will had been a charter member of the university's Arts and Sciences National Council, composed of volunteer advisers carrying out external reviews of programs, assisting and advising deans, and sharing information with the board of trustees. "The idea was to have a group of successful alumni and friends who were interested in the school and could work with us on our plans for everything we wanted to accomplish," said Dr. Edward S. Macias, executive vice chancellor and dean of Arts and Sciences. "It was not a fund-raising group. Rather, it was a sounding board for the dean, and it has been very successful. We call on the council, and on individual members, who help in a variety of ways."

When the college reorganized its career center, one of its major objectives was to focus on student internships. Several members of the council led the way by bringing interns into their businesses, or recommending the program to friends who also were in positions to do so. "Will was personally involved in all these things and many more," said Dean Macias. When administrators and faculty members wrote the draft of a strategic plan for the college, the dean took it to a meeting of the council. "Their critiques and suggestions for making it better prompted us to rewrite it," he said. "It received approval of the board of trustees and has been used as our guide ever since that time. Council members provide a degree of practical outside expertise not always available within the college, so we try to present them with special topics that will interest them, and benefit from their ideas." If Will agreed to help when asked, "as he usually does," the dean said, "he puts in the time to make it work. He is particularly interested in the Physics Department where he spent his time, but his interests go much broader than that. For instance, he always looks for things here that might be helpful for Ohio University, and vice versa. In fact, he has brought people together from the two campuses to discuss such things. Moreover, he and Ann Lee attend a great many of our activities; I see them both quite often. They also have sponsored two ongoing student scholarships in Arts and Sciences for many years."

At the request of Chancellor Danforth, Will became chairman of a special committee to examine university intellectual property policies, which hadn't been changed, or even reviewed, for thirty years. With research leading to a growing number of patents, there was no definitive way to determine equitable ownership or how licensing income should be disbursed.

Assembling a committee representing faculty, staff, the Washington University legal department, and selected outside companies, Will soon was able to provide a consensus of recommendations on how the university might solve the dilemma of ownership and deal with questions of licensing versus involvement in starting new companies. After approval by the faculty senate and university administrative leaders, a new policy was put into effect, incorporating nearly all of the committee's recommendations. Afterward, one professor, who would have been denied patent participation under the old policy because of conflicts of interest, parlayed his research discoveries into a computer technology company, sharing income with the university. Several years later, the company was sold for a sum in excess of $300 million.

The university at that time was constructing a large new natural sciences building near the landmark Brookings Quadrangle. When an appeal was made for private funding of interior sections, Will and his wife responded by providing $400,000 for one of two major well-equipped classrooms. Designed primarily for biology and psychology, McDonnell Hall was completed in 1993, with one of its prominent rooms designated the "Wilfred R. and Ann Lee Konneker Lecture Hall."

In contrast to the state university situation in Ohio, Washington University's board of trustees was made up of fifty members from around the country, most of them presidents and chief executive officers representing business, industry, publishing, education, banking and research institutes, law firms, medical and charitable associations, and entrepreneurs. "It would seem that such a large board would be unwieldy, but nearly everything was carried out through working committees, so it functioned smoothly," Will said. "A small executive committee kept things coordinated, so full board meetings primarily updated everyone on what was being accomplished." Will served on research and graduate education committees.

In 1995, Chancellor Danforth retired, and in an unprecedented move, he became chairman of the board of trustees. "Some of us naturally were skeptical," Will said, "but it worked extremely well." The new chancellor, Dr. Mark S. Wrighton, came from the Massachusetts Institute of Technology, where he had headed the Department of Chemistry and most recently held the position of provost. His administrative and research backgrounds matched the university's objectives. After reviewing research activities, the new chancellor gave Will Konneker credit for "playing a key role in developing our technology transfer activities." He added that "through the vision Dr. Konneker established, we are now well-positioned to contribute by rapidly transferring the benefits of research to our society."

For the first time in its history, the university established the position of vice chancellor for research and an entire department devoted to technology transfer. In addition to handling licensing and other legal matters, the department kept abreast of university research projects to help identify those with potential commercial value. It also provided advice on arrangements that could be made with research-funding organizations, including private companies and agencies offering government grants. As an example, Will explained, "If research is funded by a government grant, the university can get a patent on anything it develops for commercial use; the government can use it without paying royalties, but not to start a business." A wide range of individual agreements were made with corporations seeking to fund research for specified projects.

At the end of Konneker's term as a trustee, he was elected to emeritus status but continued to serve on the board. "Emeritus used to mean that a member became inactive in retirement," Dr. Danforth explained, "but now it simply means he has passed the mandatory age for regular membership. His emeritus status enables him to attend meetings, serve on committees, and generally continue as before. We are happy that Will is willing to do that, because he remains an extremely important, hard working member of our board."

In 1991, Konneker received the Distinguished Alumnus Award at the annual Washington University Founders Day banquet. The citation listed his business accomplishments and university service, noting, "He is among the first to step forward when leadership is needed." The principal banquet address was given by William H. Webster, who had just announced his intention to leave Washington and return to private life.

At the 1992 biennial international convention of Delta Tau Delta Fraternity, Konneker received the Distinguished Achievement Award for exceptional achievements in his career.

13

PICKING WINNERS

An investment in knowledge always pays the best interest.

—BENJAMIN FRANKLIN

After thirty-five years in their country home near Ellisville, Will and Ann Lee moved in 1991 to Ladue, an upscale suburban municipality of eight thousand population just west of St. Louis. The decision to relocate was neither sudden nor painless. Both had agonized over the prospect of a change for three years while they watched the city threaten to envelop their pastoral paradise that a friend once described as "a Thanksgiving house." Will in particular hesitated to succumb to what his wife referred to as "civilization creeping in much too close." She insisted that traffic on winding Kiefer Creek Road was getting heavier, and though Will didn't consider that a problem, he agreed that the area where it connected to Manchester Road was becoming highly commercialized, as were those along other routes to the city. It took longer each year to reach Washington University, the Opera Theatre, and other places of increasing involvement. Ann Lee searched for a house and property that would mollify the trauma of moving. "I found a few that Will wouldn't even look at, because there weren't enough trees and the neighbors would be too close, and those sorts of things," she said. "We had become spoiled by contentment in our rural atmosphere, I guess."

Admitting to being uncooperative while Ann Lee and a real estate agent (the daughter of a "Bridgers" friend) studied the market, made visits, and scrutinized several plausible possibilities, Will finally agreed to look at the Ladue home on Barclay Woods Drive. Situated well back from the street on three acres of trees and grass, it had a three-car garage, a spacious back patio, and a swimming pool. It would put them fifteen minutes, instead of nearly an hour, from the university and much closer to the other places they frequented. Will approved of the choice, but his wife always insisted, "I still had to drag him kicking and screaming from our other home." He accepted that analysis, as well as the realization that it was time for a change. B. Lynn, although a wife and mother living in Eureka by that time, sat in the living room of what had been "the old homestead" for her, and cried. After the move, Ann Lee never went back to look at the area, which became developed as she had predicted. "I prefer to remember it as it was," she said.

The Konnekers had their new home completely remodeled to suit personal tastes for attractiveness and utility without pretentiousness. They still were able to enjoy a variety of birds darting amongst the trees outside the glass doors leading from the breakfast area. Will was not reluctant to describe it as "a delightful place to live."

No matter how diversified and far reaching his life's interests stretched, Will Konneker never lost sight of his roots in Greenfield, Ohio. He contributed regularly and quietly to the church he attended as a youth. He never missed a Class of '40 reunion, held every five years. He and Ann Lee visited his boyhood friends in various cities and entertained them in St. Louis. He paid all costs for a 1980 book serving as an illustrated guide to works of art throughout McClain High School and helped fund other school projects. So it was not surprising that in the mid-eighties he made a codicil to his will establishing future scholarships for McClain students.

Later in the decade, however, the Konnekers decided they wanted also to set up a more immediate fund. "Ann Lee and I sat down one day and discussed how interesting it would be to see who received scholarships and maybe get to know them," Will said. Typically, they studied what was available in the state and discovered nothing in the way of a full scholarship—

tuition, room, board, and books—for anything other than athletics. "I have no problem with athletes getting full rides; I believe they deserve them," Will explained, "but we were surprised not to find any at all for academic merit."

The next time he saw President Charles Ping, Will mentioned that he wanted to do something special for the Greenfield community that was so important to his early life. Then he outlined the plan he and his wife had devised and asked for his friend's honest opinion. "I couldn't agree more," Ping replied.

Consequently, in 1990, the fiftieth anniversary of Will's high school graduation, Billy Doan of Greenfield was selected by a committee of McClain teachers to become the first recipient of a four-year "full ride" Konneker Scholarship to Ohio University. Each year thereafter another graduating senior was chosen—an arrangement that soon required concurrent endowments of four full scholarships. Will and Ann Lee not only attended recipients' high school graduations but also followed with great interest their undergraduate years at the university and their subsequent careers. (They were personally devastated when Billy Doan was killed in a traffic accident after he had graduated, taken an accounting job in Columbus, and made plans to return for an MBA degree.) This became the forerunner of an even broader program Will would come to consider the most satisfying of all their philanthropic efforts to help serve education and the future leadership of America.

The transition began with conversations between Will and Vice President Jack Ellis as they traveled together seeking contributions to the Third Century Campaign. Ellis dreamed of setting into place a premier privately endowed program that would provide a full annual scholarship for each of Ohio's eighty-eight counties. Each would be awarded in the junior year of high school. That way, Ellis said, other top students in the recipient's senior class would know the winner was going to Ohio University. He added, "I think it would be a magnet to attract other outstanding students." Konneker liked the idea, so the two men presented it to President Ping, who enthusiastically joined them in further brainstorming sessions.

The consensus they reached was to create special scholarships that would reward academic accomplishment and potential for leadership, using as a model the Morehead Awards Program, which had enhanced the academic standards, as well as the reputation, of the University of North

Carolina. Having been a graduate student working toward his Ph.D. at Duke University when nearby University of North Carolina introduced the Morehead program in 1951, Ping was familiar with how it had "dramatically changed the position of that university."

To study the concept further, Konneker, Ping, and Ellis visited the Chapel Hill campus to meet with administrators of the Morehead Awards Program. They learned that it had been limited at first to North Carolina high school students, then extended to those of other states as well. Guidelines were similar to Oxford, England's Rhodes Scholarships, except that they were adapted to undergraduate rather than graduate education. "Before many years had passed, high schools were grooming the brightest and best students as potential Morehead Scholars," Ping said. "Our hope was that the program we could establish would have that kind of impact on schools in Ohio."

North Carolina had an advantage over any other institution attempting such an expensive venture. A single 1891 alumnus, John Motley Morehead III, a noted inventor and a founder of the Union Carbide Corporation, was able to fund the entire program by donating what Konneker aptly called "stacks of Carbide stock" in the 1950s. That, to Will, was merely a logistic that Ohio University would have to overcome by spreading support among a large number of donors.

The Manasseh Cutler Scholars Program that soon developed drew from experiences with Morehead and Rhodes scholarships but was not a carbon copy of either. Named for the university's co-founder, it was designed to target high school students who demonstrated leadership potential, moral strength of character, motivation, and physical stamina, as well as academic and extracurricular achievement. Will felt strongly about the importance of those standards. "They must be good scholastically," he said, "but in addition, we want to consider what roles they have played in school activities. Have they done things that point toward becoming leaders, not only for their communities, but perhaps for the nation and the world? Society needs ethical, moral, bright leaders in all fields—teaching, business, science, politics, whatever. So we are striving to identify and encourage those kinds of future leaders."

Donors of $250,000 endowments could specify geographical areas from which their funded scholars would be chosen. Each award would carry the name of the donor who endowed it, and, although the geographic stipulation was preferred, exceptions could be made for donors preferring to specify selected academic disciplines or for funding companies nominating qualified children of employees. Will and Ann Lee planned to help launch Cutler Scholars by shifting Konneker Scholars to the new program and then to help persuade others to follow their lead.

In the midst of preliminary preparations, Dr. Ping retired in 1994 and accepted a Fulbright appointment as a research scholar surveying the roles of universities in Namibia, which had gained independence from South Africa four years earlier. He intended to return to Athens later and perhaps teach a course in philosophy, something he had continued to do during his twenty years as president. While he and his wife, Claire, were in Africa, they were visited by Will and Ann Lee. During two weeks of touring, the couples were particularly attracted to a granite burial place of Cecil John Rhodes, near Bulawayo in Zimbabwe (formerly Rhodesia). In an adjacent museum they searched chronicles of the famous British imperialist, diamond mining magnate, and education reformist, locating some of the ideas they had adapted for use in the Cutler Scholars project that remained on their minds even while enjoying their holiday respite.

Charles Ping's successor, Dr. Robert Glidden, became Ohio University's nineteenth president on July 1, 1994. Dr. Glidden, a native of Grand Junction, Iowa, received B.A., M.A., and Ph.D. degrees, all in music, from the University of Iowa. He had been at Florida State University for the past fifteen years, first as professor and dean of the School of Music, then as provost and vice president for academic affairs. Earlier in his career he had been on the faculties of Wright State and Indiana Universities and the University of Oklahoma. He also had been dean of music at Bowling Green State University and served for three years as executive director of the National Association of Schools of Music in Washington, D.C. As the university's new president, Glidden heartily endorsed the Cutler Scholars plan, which was continuing to move forward.

After Dr. Ping's year in Africa interviewing businessmen, political leaders, and students, he returned to teach and direct the Charles J. Ping Institute for the Teaching of the Humanities, created shortly before his retirement. Trustees, foundation members, and friends had donated funds to more than match a three-to-one challenge grant by the National Endowment of the Humanities, establishing the institute. The resulting endowment provided salary supplements for distinguished professors and fellows, as well as library acquisitions and special projects to further promote study in such disciplines as philosophy, history, languages, literature, archeology, and the arts.

When the Manasseh Cutler Scholars Program commenced at the beginning of the 1996–97 academic year, Ping also became its director. Headquartered in the university's Trisolini Gallery, the program began modestly with six scholarship students, four funded by the Konnekers and one each by two other major donors of many years, Beth Stocker and Jeanette Grasselli Brown. The following year added others, supported by foundation members and their wives, Alan and Ruby Riedel, Lizabeth and Charles Emrick Jr., and Alfred and Inez Corrado. Further commitments were being considered by other alumni.

In October 1997, President Glidden appointed Dr. Herman "Butch" Hill, a professor of electrical engineering, to the positions of university ombudsman and Cutler Scholars associate director. Highly respected as a popular and energetic teacher, three-term chairman of the faculty senate, and participant in a host of activities, including membership on the Konneker Scholarship Committee, Hill was dedicated to the kind of goals the scholars program hoped to reach. A board of governors, chaired by Konneker, was appointed to oversee financial needs of the new organization. Jack Ellis retired at that time, but six months later President Glidden named him part-time consultant for the program. "This became a labor of love, because I think in the long haul it might become the single most significant program ever developed at Ohio University," Ellis said.

Whenever a new award was established, a representative from the campus met with principals and counselors at eligible high schools to explain the program and its rigorous system of evaluating applicants. Individual students could not apply; they were to be nominated by school personnel or members of active alumni chapters by the end of their junior years. Regional, national, or international committees of alumni and friends then held preliminary interviews, narrowing the field to two finalists for each award by a Cutler Scholars Selection Committee on campus. Winners could enroll in any degree program, unless designated as discipline-based scholars, and would be assured of an exceptional university experience, valued at approximately $70,000, as long as they remained in good standing.

"We get amazing students," Dr. Hill said. "One of the heartbreaking things about going through the final selection process here on campus is that you can't give more Cutler Scholarships. The alternates invariably are so outstanding, you hate to leave them out." Each runner-up was informed that other types of scholarships might be available, and a statistical study later indicated that a sizable percentage of them did enroll at Ohio University.

Cutler Scholars entered their programs in the summer preceding the freshman year by taking part in Outward Bound, the acclaimed national wilderness training experience in self-reliance. Not a survival exercise, it alternated solo assignments at isolated campsites, monitored by instructors, with involvement in teamwork and a variety of service projects ranging from building trails to serving in soup kitchens. Adopted from reference to a ship leaving its home port, the term Outward Bound became a description for young people cutting loose from the safe moorings of home to grow through experiencing unfamiliar, adventurous new avenues to future responsibilities. During the three-week summer programs, instructors gradually turned responsibilities over to participants, who then could learn from the results of their own decisions.

Following the freshman year, students had summer community service stints at hospitals, police departments, and other locations where they could better understand the importance of civic responsibilities in life. After their sophomore year, they were assigned to summer jobs designed to provide firsthand experience in the way businesses operate in the capitalistic system. Because this too was funded by sponsors, program supervisors were able to select only companies that would let the students become involved, including taking part in major discussions and, as Will insisted, "not just doing things like distributing mail." In the summers before their senior years, they were given overseas assignments corresponding with the careers they planned to pursue. Both the business and overseas positions lasted about six weeks, depending on individual situations.

During each academic quarter, regular curricula were supplemented by noncredit weekly colloquia where the Cutler Scholars met as a group to discuss current affairs. Dr. Hill organized and conducted these evening meetings, with assistance from faculty and outside speakers, dealing with such topics as welfare reform, the European monetary system, capitalism and democracy, national security, gun safety, violence in the media, and workings of the United Nations. Quarterly agendas were printed and distributed in advance, with each student expected to read appropriate background material. The expressed overall focus emphasized "preparation for effective leadership in a complex society." As the number of scholars increased, the original group was divided accordingly to keep sessions conversational. Several participants told Dr. Hill the colloquia were the most important advantages of being Cutler Scholars.

In October 1998, the university announced the establishment of nineteen additional Cutler Scholarships by the Konnekers. Four were designated for students at Ann Lee's alma mater, Olean High School, four each for students in the St. Louis area, in foreign countries, and at Washington Court House. Three in the names of Jack and Sue Ellis were for students in their hometown of Chillicothe, where another scholarship already had been established. Additional tuition scholarships were funded for students who were runners-up in the competition at Greenfield's McClain High School.

By the end of the nineties, the program was not only growing but also accelerating, to the point that the board of governors and administrators informally set a new long-range goal of two hundred Cutler Scholars. Their optimism was stimulated further by exceptional records already being achieved by students in the program.

In 1999, Dr. Ping turned supervision of the institute that bore his name over to Dr. Thomas H. Carpenter, a professor of humanities and classics, but continued to direct the Cutler Scholars program. Butch Hill continued to design and direct the colloquia, and Jack Ellis coordinated funding and promotion.

The year 1996 brought two pleasant surprises to Will and Ann Lee Konneker, beginning with the golden wedding anniversary party in March. At the time of the anniversary, Ohio University's Edison Biotechnology Institute was completing its move from the West Green campus to new quarters on The Ridges, where one of the former Athens Mental Health Center patient dormitories had been transformed into a modern office and laboratory building. Unannounced plans, held in confidence by members of the board of trustees, centered on naming the building at a scheduled dedication that summer. Only a short time before the official ribbon cutting was Will Konneker told his name would be etched into the building and its future.

State, university, and city officials were among participants in the July

20, 1996, dedication of the Wilfred R. Konneker Research Laboratories, described by the *Athens Messenger* as marking "the dawn of a new era at Ohio University and The Ridges." By that time, the 40,000-square-foot building, renovated at a cost of $13.3 million, housed both the Edison Center and the university's biomolecular engineering group. President Glidden, President Emeritus Ping, and the state's Thomas Edison Program manager, Dr. Norman Chagnon, spoke at the ceremony on a brick patio outside the main entrance to the building. Ping's brief comments reflected his association with the Konnekers during his administration:

> In dedicating this building we honor a man and his contributions to Ohio University. The fit of the building and the man is quite remarkable.
>
> The building is dedicated to basic science, to research and discovery, to the work of senior and apprentice scholars in exploring new frontiers of biotechnology and bioengineering. The building bears the name of Will Konneker, who labored through the mid-years of this century as a student and a researcher in the new age of nuclear physics.
>
> The building is dedicated to directed and applied research, to exploring possibilities for the application and the use of the discoveries and the inventions of the laboratory. The building bears the name of Will Konneker, whose work in physics and whose entrepreneurial vision helped create a whole industry around nuclear diagnostics materials.
>
> The building is a restoration, preserving a part of the past of Athens; the building retains an historic grace while adding new beauty. The building bears the name of Will Konneker and with this also honors the name of Ann Lee Konneker, Will's partner in all things for over fifty years. They share a passion for historical preservation and together they have left with the Konneker Alumni Center a legacy for Ohio.
>
> The building we dedicate stands high on a hill presiding over the campus where students and faculty move from library to athletic fields, from classrooms to laboratories, from the Innovation Center to residence halls. The building stands tall and will continue to do so for many, many years to come as generations of

students and faculty come and go. The building bears the name of Will Konneker, whose dedication and labors have helped to shape Ohio University and to secure the promise of its third century of service.

How fitting that such a building dedicated to such purposes and in such a place should bear the name: the Wilfred R. Konneker Research Laboratories.

As Konneker walked from the building that now bore his name, he could remember the old "asylum grounds," where students of his era held picnics in the spring, slid down snow-covered hillsides, and ice skated on a picturesque pond in the winter. When changes in the philosophy of mental health treatment ended the use of the word *asylum* and dictated the move to a new hospital across the river, the area became a topic of discussions—sometimes heated—and negotiations, before and after much of it was deeded to the university. When definitive plans began to emerge, Will had been appointed chairman of an advisory board immersed in a series of problems and difficult decisions involving the museum of arts, named for Edwin L. Kennedy, whose collections of Navajo weavings and jewelry constituted its most substantial displays. (In 1993, the former Athens Mental Health Center administration building, in which the museum was housed, had been named Lin Hall in honor of the former dean of fine arts, Henry H. Lin.)

Complications seemed destined to haunt the museum. A $4 million state grant was expected to finance reconstruction of the first and second floors, including rooms, air-conditioning, and heating. But the budget for those plans became insufficient when it was discovered that lead paint covered most walls. "Workers had to suit up like they were going to the moon to take out those walls, collect the waste material, and dispose of it in a special way," Konneker, chair of the board, observed. Consequently, reconstruction was limited to the first floor. Moreover, a lingering question as to how the museum might best fit into the university structure persisted. To tackle these difficulties, President Glidden put together a special committee consisting of townspeople who were friends of the Trisolini Gallery, faculty and staff representatives, and others, including Konneker and noted architect Maya Lin (designer-architect of the Vietnam Veterans Memorial in Washington, D.C., an Athens native, and daughter of Dean

Henry Lin). Resolving the plethora of problems indeed would become a long-range effort, extending into early 2002, when satisfactory supervisory adjustments would result in the appointment of a new director, reporting to the dean of the College of Fine Arts.

Personnel and structural changes in other domains continued to be made on The Ridges in the last half of the nineties. Dr. David C. Wight, a research scientist who had been working with Dr. Wagner, was named interim director (later director) of the Edison Biotechnology Institute when it moved into its new building. A graduate of the University of California at Santa Barbara, with master's and doctoral degrees from the University of Michigan, he was combining his research with obtaining an MBA from the Ohio University College of Business.

David Allen was hired away from Ohio University at the beginning of 1997 to become director of technology licensing at Ohio State University (where he later became an assistant vice president). During the search for a successor, Linda J. Clark was named interim director of the Innovation Center and Transfer Office. Six months later, the university hired Gary D. Meyer to succeed Allen as assistant vice president for technology and economic development. Clark's responsibilities became focused solely on the Innovation Center, and Robert Malott concentrated on managing technology transfers.

Meyer, who earned BSEE and MBA degrees from the University of Nebraska, had organized and headed UneMed Corporation, which for the past five years had handled technology transfer operations for that university's medical center in Omaha. "One of the major things that attracted me to Ohio University was the amount of technology being commercialized through programs with modest research budgets," he said. "It was far above the national average, and when I visited the campus, it became quite apparent that the primary reasons were commitments from the foundation and top administrators. It became clear also that a driving force was Will Konneker, who was one of a small group of people who saw in the early eighties that this would be important for the future of Ohio University. Will understands that new ideas and new discoveries are the intellectual properties of a university and its individual faculty members, and it is important to take good care of these assets."

The concept of a spreading ridge-top research park, envisioned when the Innovation Center was in its infancy, was soon altered to fit the times and circumstances. Yet as new ideas were being formulated, it appeared that The Ridges would play a prominent role in research, as would other new complexes at the campus level below. Meanwhile, Will and Ann Lee Konneker were enjoying the excitement of watching Cutler Scholars progress and were looking toward results of other efforts with which they were engaged at Ohio and Washington Universities, the city of St. Louis, and even their summer vacation home at Chautauqua, where Will became a member of the institution's foundation board of directors in 1996. Topping all those lists, however, were family gratifications that increasingly focused on two growing grandchildren.

On October 7, 1995, Will and Ann Lee were among eight recipients of John C. Baker Founder's Awards, presented for the first time at a campus event celebrating the one hundredth birthday of the university's former president and the fiftieth anniversary of the fund he established. Honorees were cited for "exemplary service to the Ohio University Foundation and outstanding philanthropic support of the university." Other recipients were Fritz and Dolores Russ, Beth Stocker, Bob Axline, Gene Rinta, and the late Edwin Kennedy (whose award was accepted by his daughter, Christine Cook). More than 250 guests, including Dr. Baker, attended the campus affair, and Jeanette Grasselli Brown, a former trustee serving on the Ohio Board of Regents, as well as the Ohio University Foundation Board, presented the keynote address.

14

VANGUARDS OF TECHNOLOGY

Many of life's failures are people who did not realize how close they were to success when they gave up.

—THOMAS A. EDISON

After reviewing problems that had surfaced during early attempts to raise initial funding for Embryogen (later DNX), a group of Ohio University Foundation members, led by Will Konneker and Bob Axline, considered forming an Athens-oriented venture capital company. "Our Innovation Center essentially lost DNX to Princeton, because we had to get money from eastern venture capitalists when very little became available in Ohio," Konneker said. "We were determined not to let that happen again." Axline explained further, "We had a dream that if we could raise venture capital money, we could fund companies ourselves and therefore control them so they couldn't leave the area."

The concept was sound. A venture capital organization could raise money through sales to limited partners and use it to make equity investments in promising new technology companies. Profits returned to the venture capital founders would be donated to the foundation, which also could invest as a limited partner. Such indirect returns to Ohio University could become substantial. But there was a drawback. A partnership such as the one Konneker and Axline envisioned would have to raise several million dollars for seed-money distributions, which would require the leadership of an experienced full-time director with a salary and operational budget commensurate with the job ahead. No one in the group could assume such a time-consuming responsibility, so the idea remained dormant until 1995.

Determined to revive the plan, the group looked for a specialist who could search the marketplace for prospective venture capital investors and evaluate the probabilities of raising $10–15 million. The man they selected was Karl O. Elderkin, a 1983 mechanical engineering graduate of Cornell University with an MBA in entrepreneurial management, finance, and marketing from Wharton. He had spent six years at Texas Instruments and six years in England, where he managed fourteen venture investments of the Generics Group, a leading integrated technology consulting, development, and financial subscription organization.

Elderkin accepted the assignment, made his survey, and delivered a thumbs-up report. On February 20, 1997, the Ohio Valley Venture Fund limited partnership became fully operational, with the energetic thirty-eight-year-old Elderkin hired as managing partner. The general partner was made up of two entities: a one-member KOE Investment Company (Elderkin) and South East Enterprise Development Fund, Inc., established specifically for the enterprise as a not-for-profit company known by the acronym SEED. Authority for management of the general partner was vested in an eight-member board of directors, seven appointed by SEED, and Elderkin. An executive committee was empowered to make most board decisions between full meetings. Its original members were Konneker, as chairman, Axline, and Jerry F. Peppers, a 1968 alumnus, internationally known New York City lawyer, and frequent media commentator on acquisition and takeover issues.

Although the entire SEED board was composed of current or former members of the Ohio University Foundation, it was not tied legally to the foundation, nor to the university. Partnership documents made that point clear. Neither organization could be held liable for Ohio Valley Venture Fund obligations. Moreover, the fund board took strong measures to avoid any semblance of competing with the foundation. The latter provided $350,000 in start-up capital and became one of several limited partners. But its involvement was strictly a business transaction to create profits, along with those from other investments. Prospects were particularly sound, because members of SEED were prepared to absorb losses, yet donate general manager gains to the foundation. As with the Innovation Center itself, opposing voices were heard from segments of the public. "We live in a society where it is unusual—not unique, but unusual—to find people who do things for others without expecting anything beyond satisfaction for themselves," Axline said. "So there are skeptics, and that is perfectly understandable."

Difficult explanations to detractors soon became moot as the venture capital group's progress unfolded. Elderkin, sometimes accompanied by Konneker, set out to raise limited partnership money. By the end of its first year Ohio Valley Venture Fund raised eight and a half million dollars from twenty-eight partners, one of them the Ohio University Foundation. By the year 2000, this had grown to $11.3 million—of which $1.3 million came from the foundation—fully invested in eleven companies.

In locating embryonic companies for investments, the venture group put preferential priorities on those within Ohio and surrounding midwestern states. Feasibility, however, dictated that it expand those horizons to such areas as California's Silicon Valley, where extraordinary capital gains were most apt to be gained at that time. There was no thought of moving the venture capital headquarters from Athens, but investments had to be based on making the best possible commitments, wherever they might appear. Elderkin explained the philosophy and modus operandi of the Ohio Valley Venture Fund:

> The typical process is that organizers of a new company will invest some of their own savings to acquire or develop a technology, then search out further money from family and friends, doctors and dentists, and angels, usually in that order. When they get to the stage of proving their concept, and have put together a strong management team, but need more financing, they have ammunition to convince us they can make it a commercial success. At that point, we can really help professionalize the process. Sometimes they have people with far more knowledge of technology than experience in the commercial arena, so they ask for more than just financial support. We do a lot more than just put in money. We help build the company. We might even go out and

help find more deep-pocketed investors. Sometimes an angel investor who has heard of us through friends will approach us with his conviction that a prospective company has the best thing he has ever seen. He can't afford the total dollars needed, but hopes we might invest also and use our expertise to raise additional funding. In fact, some of our best deals come from things like that. There is no set pattern, because there are so many variations.

One of the budding companies, Pain Therapeutics, understandably attracted Will Konneker's special attention. Researchers at Albert Einstein Hospital had studied opiates, with the hope of discovering how their exceptional pain-killing properties could be utilized without producing undesirable side effects, including addiction. During their investigations, they found that two critical receptors on the surface of human cells dealt with morphine and other opioids. One type relieved pain and the other seemed to cause addiction. If there were some way to block one effect and admit the other into a cell, the result could produce a new generation of powerful yet safe drugs offering benefits not found in existing analgesics. In time, they did find a combination that appeared to meet such a requirement, but their focus did not go beyond research into the three long, involved series of stages necessary for FDA approval. Remi Barbier, a West Coast entrepreneur who already had developed and sold three small biotechnology companies, saw this as another opportunity. Using money from those sales, he negotiated a licensing agreement with Einstein Hospital and took the product through phase 1, demonstrating that the drug seemed to work. To move into phase 2 and 3 requirements for exhaustive studies of data and patents, extensive testing on hundreds, then thousands of patients to receive FDA approval, and finally advancing into production and marketing, he needed to attract substantial backing.

Ohio Valley Venture Fund subsequently became the first and primary outside investor in Pain Therapeutics, Inc., which was based in south San Francisco. Because of Konneker's interest and involvement, as well as his position as chairman of the Ohio Valley Venture Fund board, he became a director of the new corporation in November 1999. The experience was somewhat reminiscent of his personal activities with Nuclear Consultants, Inc., and FDA procedures nearly fifty years earlier, as well as the start-ups of Embryogen and Diagnostic Hybrids.

In June 2000, eight months after the Venture Fund made a $1.2 million investment in Pain Therapeutics, the company went public. Shares received by the fund soared to a value of $14 million, which could not be distributed immediately because of a lock-up clause. It decreased considerably during the market collapse that followed, when some companies lost 90 percent of their value. Yet even with that plunge, the investment increased fourfold in less than two years. A second company in which a $1 million investment had been made in 1988 was preparing to go public three years later, when it was purchased by Hewlett-Packard, converting partnership money into company securities. Another also was sold at a profit, but a fourth, a petrochemical processor, earlier had encountered financial problems when the price of oil skidded to an all-time low and was sold at a loss of $300,000.

In spite of the disastrous stock market decline, by the end of 2001 the Ohio University Foundation received twice the amount of its $1.3 million investment, with seven companies remaining in the portfolio of the fund, which was renamed Athenian Venture Partners I. These were slated to be realized (liquidatable but not necessarily liquidated) in 2006. "We prefer to distribute securities so recipients can either sell or hold them," Elderkin explained. Unlike an evergreen fund in which generated gains are recycled into further investments, Partnership I was a call fund with a set life.

The fund manager described Konneker as playing a significant role both as a general partner board member and a mentor. "I'm on the phone with him several times a week," Elderkin said. "I've been in investment management for twenty years, but when we have to make decisions, he is the first person I go to for an opinion. He has a lot of sage advice and a lot of experience."

An overlapping Athenian Venture Partners II was launched in 2001. By the end of the year it had raised $30 million, about half of its goal, and invested in four companies. The foundation again became a limited partner with an investment of $1 million. Elderkin expected Partners III to be started within the following three years.

After struggling for nearly two decades, Diagnostic Hybrids, the Innovation Center's first company, entered the new century as its most prominent rising star. It had dipped in the mid-nineties to a level of three employees and $10,000 through a series of unfortunate events. At its depth, when

DNA kits appeared unable to penetrate much of the marketplace, a decision was made to glance backward at early expertise and consider selling just the live cells that were needed for research and diagnosis. That was done and business grew slightly.

But David Scholl, who had become president of the company in 1995, with Will remaining active as chairman of the board of directors and close confidant, envisioned something far greater. "What if you go into those cells and genetically change them in some way, so that when a virus comes in and upsets the cell, a signal of some kind will detect it?" David asked himself and Will.

"Excellent idea," was the shared answer.

Without hesitation and with great enthusiasm, Scholl prepared a detailed plan and proposal for the National Institutes of Health, federal distributor of grants and contracts for scientific research. Almost as quickly, Diagnostic Hybrids got a discouraging reply, essentially describing the idea as outlandish. About six months later, a professional journal reported that a professor at Washington University in St. Louis had done exactly what Scholl had suggested.

Admittedly miffed at the National Institutes of Health's decision, Scholl and Konneker obtained a license from Washington University for the genetically engineered cells and moved ahead with the plan. The licensing agreement gave Diagnostic Hybrids exclusive worldwide commercial development rights to patented transgenic cell technology leading to a product that was to become known as ELVIS. "The name was an acronym for Enzyme Linked Virus Inducible System," Will said, "but it's eye-catching appeal certainly was helpful from a marketing point of view. Suddenly our product was commercially viable, and business just took off."

Viruses taken directly from patient samples are not sufficient to test. ("If you had enough viruses in you to test, you probably would be dead," Will explained.) ELVIS provided a means of amplifying the virus in a patient's sample, using live cells in layers that were incubated to allow the virus to multiply, just as it would do in a body, until there were enough to measure. A highly simplified explanation of the technology was its ability to target infected cells, treat them, and read results with a conventional light microscope. Scholl described it as "simple to use, but highly sensitive for a one-day detection of herpes infections." Harking back to fruitful techniques Will had developed for his own company, the group put together complete diagnostic kits that included all necessary ingredients, including the live cells. These cells were genetically engineered to both speed the growth of viruses and produce a protein that changed color, furthering the efficacy of detection. ELVIS test kits soon accounted for half of company sales, but other products did well also. Among them were FreshCells, FreshFrozen Cells, DNA probe kits, and other innovative cell culture products for various applications in diagnostic virology and endocrine diseases.

Marketing became worldwide. "Will took me to Europe twice and introduced me to business there, and he took me to St. Louis for my first business licensing," Scholl said. "I thought about all the other things he had to do, but this was *so* important to him. It epitomized the whole concept of getting a commercial economic development strategy going for this region and the university he loves for sure. So we're in virology. We make cell cultures. And we have customers ordering over and over again. That is what Will considers the validation of business. Until then, he says, you haven't made it because you're not sustainable. Grant to grant to grant is kind of like molecular welfare of sorts." Despite his hectic schedule as president of the company, Scholl visited clients around the country to instruct them in the best use of Diagnostic Hybrids products and help alleviate specific difficulties. Sales reached $1 million in 1999, $2 million in 2000, and well over $4 million in 2001, setting a pattern of growth that would continue.

As the twentieth century came to a close, the original thought of a research park on The Ridges was abandoned, as expected. Konneker Research Laboratory activities were moving forward well as headquarters for the Edison Biotechnology Institute. But development of an expansive research complex in that area had become less feasible in terms of cost analyses and practicalities. This became increasingly evident when contrasted with the availability of more than sixty-five acres of level land at the foot of West State Street. Long abandoned by the McBee Company, the majority of the property had been owned by the university since 1901. Renovations of remaining buildings on The Ridges were considered more suitable for other plans, including a Voinovich Center for Leadership in Public Affairs, a child care center, graduate art studios for painting, and various academic support groups. John Kotowski, vice president for facilities planning, also located there, provided insight into short- and long-range projections for The Ridges:

> The fact that the main campus is basically "built out" (meaning there are few locations to build, limiting Ohio University's ability to grow and keep pace with the needs of higher education in Ohio), makes The Ridges attractive to the University for rehabilitation. And it is a good location for non-academic functions. By renovating the facilities at The Ridges, the University puts itself in a better position of freeing space on the main part of the campus for its academic and research needs. For this reason, the adaptive re-use of the buildings at The Ridges makes sense as long as the appropriate functions can be found. In the short term, the plan of the University is to renovate the cottages and "out type" buildings for various smaller units. Units like mine (the facilities planning and construction operation), that require offices, office support, and conference-type spaces, work quite well in the buildings of the former mental health center. The main building at The Ridges is more challenging. This building was intended to be very secure with only one way in, that being the main entrance into the administration unit, now occupied by the Kennedy Museum. In order for the remainder of the building, namely the two large wings, to be useful, new entries need to be added. It is my hope that this will be a lead step in bringing the rest of the building back into use. Without them, the wings are useful only for storage. With proper entryways, they will have multi-type uses, such as offices on the first levels and housing on the upper floors. (Construction on the first such entry was begun in the summer of 2002.)

In 1977, a modern facility had been constructed for the College of Engineering and Technology's Center for Corrosion in Multiphase Systems at the West State Street site, later to be known as Enterprise and Research Park. One-half of a second building, designed to become a bioscience center, was scheduled for occupancy by Diagnostic Hybrids, through a five-year lease agreement. In 2001, a year in which Diagnostic Hybrids' income reached $5 million, the company moved into the new quarters, leaving its former building once again a deserted campus landmark awaiting either the wrecking ball of progress or the infusion of capital funds to extend its useful life.

Soon after the move, Scholl reported that the company was producing cell cultures at an annualized rate of 2.5 million in 189 lines and formats, contrasting those figures with the early days when Konneker's personal financing kept the business alive in the face of seemingly great odds. "I try to think of ways to describe what Will does," he said, "and I conclude that he invests in self-discovery. Not his own self. It's the self-discovery of the people and the institutions he invests in. When he invests time, effort, and capital in a university program, whether it is technology, or music, or other arts, it becomes a challenge to see what can be accomplished. So people don't like to let Will down."

James Brown, senior vice president and chief operating officer of the company, concurred. After receiving bachelor's and master's degrees from the University of Missouri and attending the University of Oregon, Jim joined Will's St. Louis company, Nuclear Consultants, as head of research and development in 1963. He remained in that position when the company was merged into Mallinckrodt, but in 1984 he accepted another offer from Will, this time to become part of Diagnostic Hybrids in Athens. Seventeen years later, he looked back at "a striking parallel between our company today and Will's company nearly four decades ago." Nuclear Consultants was in a period of rapid growth at that time, he recalled, "making our own products, developing new ones, and growing so rapidly that larger companies with resources for even greater expansion had their eyes on us. It was very exciting, and we are that way at DHI now."

One of Diagnostic Hybrids' major competitors was BioWhittaker, Inc., an eastern company that had been bought and later spun off by a larger West Coast corporation, to become the nation's primary supplier of live cells. When ELVIS, with its genetically engineered cells, became recognized as the superior product on the market, Scholl and Konneker offered BioWhittaker exclusive marketing rights to all hospitals in the United States and Europe. Diagnostic Hybrids, which had other projects under way, would retain such rights with the country's two major laboratory chains, which it needed for clinical research. In exchange, BioWhittaker would loan Diagnostic Hybrids $750,000 and pay royalties, to be deducted from that debt. BioWhittaker would have two years to make enough sales to generate the necessary royalties. If that obligation was not accomplished, Diagnostic Hybrids' obligation would be dissolved. Initially, BioWhittaker executives insisted that if such a "wild proposal" could be accepted, they would want to buy out Diagnostic Hybrids. Will's answer was, "Absolutely not; I'm not even going to discuss the idea." Finally, BioWhittaker agreed to the terms, with the provision that the buyout could be discussed at a later date. It also increased the loan to Diagnostic Hybrids by $1 million to support further research. After some turnover in management, however, BioWhittaker was purchased by Cambrex Corporation of East Rutherford, New Jersey, a company with broad enough interests that it paid only partial attention to ELVIS sales. Seeing an opportunity, Diagnostic Hybrids offered to purchase part of that company's BioWhittaker division. After lengthy negotiations, Diagnostic Hybrids in early 2002 bought back not only the marketing rights of ELVIS but also the cell business that had been part of BioWhittaker, using the money it had received through the loan arrangement in which most of the payback had been erased by unfulfilled sales agreements. A February 21, 2002, news release provided details:

> Diagnostic Hybrids Inc. today announced it has closed on the acquisition of the *in vitro diagnostic* cell culture product line of BioWhittaker Inc., a division of Cambrex Corporation. . . . The acquisition represents an effort by Diagnostic Hybrids and Bio-Whittaker to bring the most innovative cell culture products to clinical virologists in the United States, Canada, and Europe. It allows for an orderly transition of BioWhittaker cell culture interests to Diagnostic Hybrids, permitting BioWhittaker to focus on other strategic directions while Diagnostic Hybrids continues to grow and enhance its customer service and technology as the leading provider worldwide of genetically engineered and routine tissue cell culture lines and accessories for a wide range of clinical diagnostic purposes. . . . Products are made up to three times per week and provided in several formats, including tubes, shell vials, multi-well plates, flasks, and frozen cell suspensions. Multiple manufacturing days allow customers more

flexibility in placing orders. Others in the industry require pre-notification of up to two weeks.

Following the closing, President Scholl speculated that Diagnostic Hybrids would "remain aggressive in its attempts to consolidate other business opportunities in the clinical virology marketplace." (The company continued its rapid rate of growth, predicting income of $14 million for the year 2002.)

Diagnostic Hybrids activities of Scholl and Konneker led to friendships with Dr. Leonard Kohn, renowned researcher at the National Institutes of Health, who shared their belief in commercializing basic science discoveries obtained in educational laboratories. During thirty-six years with the Washington-based NIH, Kohn developed drugs to prevent the autoimmune system from damaging organs of people suffering from Graves' disease, lupus, and diabetes. He also was interested in developing diagnostic tools to detect such viral diseases as AIDS in early stages. As a sideline to his research, he had founded a privately owned, nonprofit company, Interthyr Corporation, that purchased products from Diagnostic Hybrids. Scholl and Konneker believed Ohio University could gain an academic coup if it could accomplish the seemingly impossible task of luring Kohn to the position of distinguished senior research scientist with its Edison Biotechnology Institute. University administrators agreed to make such an effort, the result of which was reported in the winter 2001 issue of *Ohio Today* by assistant editor Melissa Rake:

> In a unique move, Ohio University pooled funds from public and private sources to present Kohn a package he couldn't refuse. His position is supported by a $900,000 grant from the state's Technology Action Fund and a $1.97 million investment from the University, The Ohio University Foundation, and private companies, including Diagnostic Hybrids, Inc. . . . The money will support not only Kohn's salary, but space in Konneker Research Labs, equipment, and an international research team of six post-doctoral fellows and a visiting scientist. Besides doing research, the medical doctor will teach and mentor graduate and undergraduate students and collaborate with the College of Osteopathic Medicine to conduct clinical trials based on his research.

In addition to joining other prominent research scientists at the institute, Kohn made his Interthyr Corporation part of the Innovation Center. This combination had a special meaning for Konneker, because it personified the long-range goals he had hoped for in suggesting the creation of an Innovation Center twenty years earlier. Kohn's presence was certain to attract researchers and grants to the university and perhaps encourage development of more new businesses in the region. In addition, he was qualified to teach subjects in the College of Osteopathic Medicine that were not previously available. "Dr. Konneker was instrumental in my coming to Ohio University," Kohn said. "He was most persuasive."

With a decision having been made to increase emphasis on incubation of embryonic companies, while scaling back on what may have been overly ambitious thoughts of expanding into a sweeping research-industrial assemblage, the Innovation Center was slated for a second relocation, this time to Enterprise and Research Park.

Linda Clark, who had been promoted to director of the center in September 2000, wrote grants that obtained a total of $3 million from the U.S. Development Administration and Appalachian Regional Commission for the new building, expected to be completed in 2003. An additional $200,000 was obtained from the U.S. Department of Agriculture for equipment to be shared among the biotechnology companies.

The two-story building would provide 35,000 square feet—triple the previous amount—with expanded laboratory space and facilities to handle light manufacturing start-ups and a wide range of prototype developments for biotechnology, information technology, service, and various other business categories.

"Many people don't realize how much impact Will Konneker has in terms of job creation within this community," Clark said. "It multiplies. We are getting a new building. We are getting technical assistance for this region. There is a venture capital system in place. The things we need to move ahead are coming about. And that is thanks to Will."

In late 2002, WALID, Inc., a privately held company headquartered in Ann Arbor, Michigan, announced its opening of a research and development office in the Innovation Center as one element of a partnership with Ohio University's Russ College of Engineering and Technology. The company, which provided systems enabling businesses, organizations, and individuals to conduct Internet global commerce by communicating in any language, was headed by CEO Cruse W. Moss, a 1948 industrial engineering graduate and recipient of an honorary doctorate for a long list of varied services and contributions to Ohio University. He and Will had been colleagues on both the foundation board and the Engineering and Technology Board of Visitors, and in special university fund-raising efforts. In addition, Moss and his wife, Virginia, sponsored three Cutler Scholarships.

The addition of WALID brought the Innovation Center total to eighteen resident businesses and one affiliate receiving all benefits of the program but not located at the center. More than 625 jobs had been created through center activities, Clark reported, and seven companies had been spun off from university developed/supported technology. Faculty and staff members had started twenty-one companies. In addition to providing space, facilities, and equipment, the center sponsored educational workshops and seminars targeted to new business development and access to consulting faculty members. "We have technical assistance available also," Clark explained. "We hire experts to work with each start-up company in identifying markets, determining how to reach them, how to sell, and how to meet legal and government regulations. There are many options."

Clients ranged from the state's only company manufacturing modular buildings for both commercial and residential structures and another providing technical support for the welding robotics industry, to videotape producers, and Internet marketers. In each instance, a company was expected to create jobs and demonstrate a high growth potential, maintaining procedures to provide monthly profit and loss statements. Failure to do so could result in termination of the agreement.

The Edison Biotechnology Institute too was arranging to widen its spectrum of support for faculty researchers, particularly in fields of life sciences, who were interested in developing their discoveries into marketable products. At a November 29, 2000, press conference, university president Glidden had announced a new partnership between EBI and Battelle, a renowned international nonprofit, nonstock research corporation based in Columbus. EBI director Wight believed the collaboration would provide "a new avenue" for assisting faculty "beyond the boundaries" of the institute and lead to much larger cooperative ventures with Battelle. Dialogue during negotiations for the collaborative venture had revealed similar strategic visions of how business and higher education could combine expertise to accelerate the nation's scientific, cultural, and economic advancement.

With a staff of 7,500 scientists, engineers, and support specialists, located at technology centers, offices, and other facilities in more than forty cities around the world, Battelle had an annual business volume approaching $1 billion. Typically, its work resulted in fifty to one hundred patented inventions each year. Organized as Battelle Memorial Institute in 1929, it became best known for playing crucial roles in developing the office copier machine (Xerox), optical digital recording that led to the compact disc, bar code symbols used on grocery packaging, and electronic commerce technologies for banks. It held 250 patents relating to the dry-copying process alone.

To nourish its momentum in private support, the Ohio University Foundation unveiled a twenty-first century agenda revealing a capital gifts campaign even more ambitious than the one it had completed in 1993. The bicentennial campaign, announced publicly at a November 11, 2000, kickoff gala on campus, was expected to raise an appropriate $200 million in time for the 200th anniversary of the university's 1804 founding. More than half the money, university president Robert Glidden said, would be used to attract "renowned scholars, outstanding professors, and promising students," by financing endowed chairs, named professorships, scholarships, and fellowships. Other funds would be channeled to campus additions, such as "cutting-edge technology and a 'smart' classroom building featuring the latest electronic capabilities," he said. "It will strengthen innovative programming and support important initiatives, including our many and varied international pursuits and those that reach out to serve our southeastern Ohio neighbors." Foundation trustees James Daley and Charles Emrick, who were named campaign co-chairmen, already had worked tirelessly to receive off-stage gifts and commitments of $114 million. Among these was the largest single gift commitment in the university's history, at least $20 million from Frank and Margaret Krasovec of Austin, Texas. A 1965 graduate with a 1966 MBA, Mr. Krasovec was the founder of Norwood Promotional Products, the world's largest supplier of promotional items, with fourteen manufacturing and printing plants in the United States and Canada, and sales to some fifteen thousand independent distributors.

Daley, a 1963 graduate and current chairman of the foundation board, was executive vice president and chief financial officer of EDS, the world's second-largest computer service provider. Emrick, who earned bachelor's and master's degrees in 1951 and 1952, and a J.D. from Cleveland Marshall Law School (later part of Cleveland State University) in 1958, was senior vice president and managing director of the Trans-Action Group, a Cleveland investment banking firm. He was chairman of the Ohio University Board of Trustees in 1996–97 and Alumnus of the Year in 2000.

Appointed to membership on the campaign executive committee, Will attended all the meetings. Not surprisingly, he and Ann Lee made an early pledge of $2.5 million to create College of Arts and Sciences endowments for a specialized faculty chair and for graduate students in the final stages of writing their dissertations. Dean Leslie Fleming planned to earmark income from the estate gift to advance interdisciplinary teaching and research in the sciences. "We have a great many projects that cross traditional departmental lines," she said. "In the whole area of life sciences today there is a convergence of people in different disciplines."

From his own experience as a nuclear physicist and businessman, Will was a longtime vocal advocate of study and research across multiple disciplines. He had witnessed its effectiveness at Washington University and at one time brought an Ohio University provost to St. Louis to discuss it with faculty and administrators there. "Things have become too complicated for a single field of expertise," he said. "You sometimes need an array of disciplines to make a complete study—perhaps a chemist and a physicist, and maybe an engineer and a computer scientist. Students could be taught the same way. And I don't see it as pertaining just to science. If you are teaching history of a foreign country, you should tie in the language and the literature so students don't get something in abstraction, but get the whole picture. I know Ohio University is doing some of these things now, and I want to back such efforts by the College of Arts and Sciences."

The new campaign gift brought total Konneker donations and bequests in support of Ohio University programs to well over $14 million, some of which had never been announced publicly because of their preference for anonymity. "I think Will was touched in his younger days by people who influenced him and helped him reach goals," observed Leonard R. Raley, vice president for university advancement, which included development, communications, and alumni affairs. "I think he has never forgotten that. Ann Lee is that way too. They share a sincere interest in seeing young people reach potentials they might not have realized were there. They want to find ways to help create the next generation of leaders. These values are consistent with the best measure of true philanthropists—those who do it for the joy of seeing the benefits that come to others, without calling attention to themselves."

In April 1998, Will accepted an invitation to join the board of visitors of the Ohio University College of Engineering and Technology. Two years later, he became vice chairman, and in 2001 he was elected chairman. During his chairmanship, he and Ann Lee established a $25,000 endowment to support undergraduate research in biomedical engineering.

15

A BROAD VIEWPOINT

*Only as you know yourself can your brain
serve you as a sharp and efficient tool.*
—BARNARD M. BARUCH

The Konnekers spent the summer of 2001 at Chautauqua, where Will enjoyed taking long walks along narrow streets winding through the 740-acre community of one thousand property owners and more than seven thousand summer visitors. He had become involved as a member of the Chautauqua Foundation, helping to reorganize the group's investment philosophy to inject more diversification into a $42 million fund. He also was busy helping raise money in support of cultural events and first-rate facilities of boys' and girls' clubs on the community's South Campus. Yet a laptop computer and telephone kept him in regular touch with secretary Sue Winter in St. Louis, as well as persons directing eleven separate organizations with which he was actively affiliated.

None of those activities kept Will from attending daily lectures presented by knowledgeable leaders on widespread topics, nor going with Ann Lee three evenings a week to hear the Chautauqua Symphony Orchestra, made up of professionals from around the country. They also saw performances of the Chautauqua Opera Company, visiting ballet troupes and a variety of other outside groups ranging from big bands and Irish dancers to folk singers and country-music combos. Each Monday they attended a concert by a youth orchestra comprised of talented high school and college students, many with scholarships to attend Chautauqua's summer-long seminars. Similar opportunities were available to outstanding students in dance, theater, and visual arts who had competed for scholarships through nationwide auditions early in the year. Religion, too, was the basis for daily programming, just as it had been for the past 127 years.

Magazine and newspaper travel writers were attracted to what one labeled "The World of Chautauqua," adding to its recognition as a truly American institution combining the pleasures of arts, study, serious and light entertainment, lakeside living, water sports, self-improvement, and community camaraderie. On one of his flights, Will opened a copy of *USAir Magazine* and was surprised to see a full-page photograph of "The Konneker House" illustrating an article about the spirit of Chautauqua. The much-traveled Konnekers agreed with claims by many other summer residents, some of them sixth-generation Chautauquans, that the atmosphere there was true to its professed original mission of uplifting the human spirit while remaining sensitive to the times.

Two weeks after returning home from Chautauqua, Will and Ann Lee prepared to leave again, this time on a flight to Tokyo, where members of the St. Louis Opera Theatre were scheduled to present a Japanese opera, "Tale of Genji." Will, who recently had chaired a successful $10 million capital gifts campaign for the Opera Theatre, was invited, along with his wife, to join a group of other board members and patrons at three Tokyo performances and related social events. But the departure date was September 13, 2001. Fortunately, the opera company had made the trip five days earlier.

With airline flights temporarily canceled throughout America following the September 11 terrorists attacks on the World Trade Center and Pentagon, the Konnekers' plans at first seemed to be in jeopardy. After spending most of the night in the St. Louis airport, they were able to board a flight to Dallas-Fort Worth, arriving just in time for their connection to Tokyo. Despite the tensions felt around the world, the opera's trip was a complete success. Each of three performances on consecutive nights brought full-house attendance and a standing ovation.

Will and Ann Lee remained in Tokyo for a week, attending a six-hour performance of Kabuki, the famed centuries-old traditional form of Japanese theater, and accompanying their longtime friends, the Ogawas and Yoshidas, to Izu Peninsula, where they enjoyed *onsen,* a natural hot-spring bath, at Shuzen-ji, a famous resort. ("They ate only Japanese food, as usual, when they were in our country," said Hiroshi Ogawa.) Afterward, they flew on to Beijing, China, joining the opera entourage for another week before returning to St. Louis.

Will quickly became immersed in an ongoing project that was proving to be the most formidable fund-raising effort of his philanthropic career. The St. Louis Symphony Orchestra, despite its ranking as one of the five best in the nation, faced what Board Chairman Virginia Weldon described as "the most critical juncture in its history." As with most major performing arts organizations, the 121-year-old symphony raised about 30 percent of its operating expenses from ticket sales, the rest coming from donations, grants, and, most important, endowment income. While expanding its programming through the years—concerts, community outreach programs, and symphony music schools for children and adults—deficits had accumulated to a dangerous level. To not only preserve its world-class stature, but simply to survive, it mounted a major capital gifts campaign. As board of trustees treasurer and executive committee member, Konneker was vitally involved.

Ironically, the orchestra had received international media attention at the beginning of the year with the announcement of the largest single challenge grant ever offered to an American symphony. The family of Jack Taylor, founder and chairman of St. Louis–based Enterprise Rent-A-Car, committed a gift of $40 million if it could be matched by other contributions within four years. If carried out, the assignment could provide a greatly enlarged endowment assuring solid long-term financial footing. Treasurer Konneker and other trustees were determined to meet, and indeed surpass, the challenge by raising new funds at an unprecedented pace.

Consequently, that undertaking rose to the top of Will's fall 2001 agenda, together with duties as chairman of the Sheldon Concert Hall Board. The Sheldon had completed a major $5 million expansion project in 1998, converting its adjacent three-story parking garage into an addition containing two reception areas, a sculpture garden, seven-thousand square feet of galleries for architectural, jazz, and children's art exhibits, and a third-floor meeting room that could accommodate five hundred people for dinner. A large parking lot had supplanted the spiraling garage inclines designed in an era of narrow vehicles, and elevators in the revamped edifice took patrons from the ground level to a walkover ramp leading into the historic concert hall. Will had been involved, both financially and as a member of the facilities committee during the reconstruction period, which enhanced the Sheldon tremendously but understandably created a sizable deficit, including budgets for increased operating and maintenance costs. When he was elected chairman at the beginning of 2001, the program had been operating in the red since the additions were made. Determined to change that predicament, he led the way in achieving a surplus in the first year, and another when he continued as chairman in 2002.

At the same time, Will remained chairman of the rapidly expanding Diagnostic Hybrids and continued his usual melange of other business responsibilities. Asked to analyze the personal financial earnings represented on his saturated calendar, he studied it briefly and answered, "I think I'm a working member of eleven boards, none of which brings me a cent; and my dollar a year (the Innovation Center agreement of 1983) has been cut off."

Will Konneker was sensitive to the possibility that his career and subsequent participation in technologically oriented aspects of higher education could be construed by some to indicate he positioned research above teaching. Knowing that his records of support and involvement refuted any such misconception, however, he never tried to debate the topic. It was not in his nature to waste time taking defensive measures against vagaries he knew in his own mind to be false. Friends and colleagues understood this. Said one, "In the time some persons would spend trying to convince doubters, Will would be moving ahead to something else." Jack Ellis, who continued to work part time with Ohio University's Cutler Scholars program, agreed. "Will never let himself get bogged down in minutia," he said. "He always looked at the broad picture and got things done."

Cutler Scholars themselves provided ample gratification for the Konnekers, as well as other sponsors. Will was particularly pleased when some of the student scholars combined their studies with practical applications at Diagnostic Hybrids, exemplifying one of the benefits he always had promoted as an auxiliary asset of an innovation center.

Heather Baird, a graduate of Greenfield's McClain High School, was a member of the Pilot Group, a name given to the first six Cutler Scholars. Although she majored in chemistry, Heather wanted to get experience in business as a possible field for her minor. Consequently, she received a position with Diagnostic Hybrids during the summer following her sophomore year, fulfilling the business internship phase of the scholars program. Given the assignment of conducting a manufacturing cost analysis, she delved into the necessary research and emerged with a new cost accounting system that astounded both Konneker and President Scholl to the extent that it was adopted immediately. At Scholl's request, she continued part-time work with the company at the start of her junior year, becoming fascinated with the technology of cell culturing. By spring, she was offered an opportunity to carry out the next summer's overseas assignment at a laboratory in Udine, Italy, where Diagnostic Hybrids had a business connection. Accepting exuberantly, Heather added an Italian language course to her already full third-quarter schedule. Then, as a laboratory researcher at the University of Udine's Institute of Clinical Pharmacology and Toxicology that summer, she was able to introduce new biochemistry approaches to faculty and students. An incredulous Will Konneker observed, "She had just finished her junior year at Ohio University, and here she was in a foreign nation, lecturing to graduate students and faculty on new technology." Back at Ohio for her senior year, she again worked for Diagnostic Hybrids, conducting research and publishing papers in scientific journals. By the time she received her degree in chemistry/biochemistry in June 2000, she had been accepted for graduate studies at Harvard, Johns Hopkins, Stanford, and Case Western Reserve Universities. She chose the latter, enrolling in a dual MBA/Ph.D. program in pharmacology.

Another Greenfield McClain graduate, biochemistry student Tyler Chamblin, followed Heather's footsteps to a business internship at Diagnostic Hybrids, where he helped develop a new Graves' disease assay. Traveling to Australia the following summer for his overseas assignment, he worked in Medvet Science virology laboratory at Adelaide. Much of his time there was spent demonstrating Diagnostic Hybrids cell culture and virus detection products. "He did so well," David Scholl said, "that the Australian group initiated a program using our line of products." After receiving his B.S. degree in 2001, Tyler began a Ph.D. program in pharmacology/genetics at Ohio State University but left to join Diagnostic Hybrids as a full-time research scientist. In 2002, he also began working during off-duty hours toward an MBA at Ohio University.

Allison Norwood, a Riedel-Cutler Scholar, from Bridgeport, Ohio, also followed a summer internship at Diagnostic Hybrids with continued lab assignments during her junior year at Ohio University. For her study/work experience abroad, she served as a research intern at the Eijkman-Winkler Institute in the Netherlands. Her job with the institute's Department of Virology focused on antiviral resistance of Herpes Simplex Virus and HIV. Directors of the project were so impressed with her work that they sent one of their research scientists to Athens, where he worked with those at Diagnostic Hybrids. A biological science major, she followed graduation in 2001 with enrollment in the Ohio State University College of Medicine.

Will was no less proud of Cutler Scholars who majored in subjects outside the realm of science. Alanna Beatty of Greenfield, who was a junior when the program started and who had already received a Konneker scholarship, majored in elementary education and received high praise from New Zealand's Spreydon Primary School in Christchurch, where she did her practice teaching during the summer following her junior year. After graduation in 1998, she became a teacher in Knoxville, Tennessee, while working toward a master's degree through Ohio University's Elementary Teaching Fellows program. Greenfield's Cary Bishop interned at Northboro, Massachusetts, with Plastic Card Systems, Inc., owned by Bob Axline, and spent his overseas assignment at Japan's Chubu University. Following graduation in 2000, he was a White House intern with the Office of the Vice President and involved with the presidential campaign for five months. He then began studies in international law at Ohio State.

Will and Ann Lee could name all of their sponsored scholarship students in order—including those who had preceded the Cutler program. They corresponded with all of the young men and women, both students and alumni, and kept photographs of them in their St. Louis home. They looked forward to receiving the letters and holiday cards, and Will traveled to Greenfield for each year's McClain High School commencement, where he presented scholarships to new winners. Their belief in the impact such projects could exert in helping find answers to world problems never faded. It was, in fact, reinforced by reports from scholarship students following their experiences abroad.

Sponsorship became international when Risto Gusterov, one of the most highly respected entrepreneurs in the Republic of Macedonia, endowed two Cutler Scholarships for students from that small European nation. Although he had not been educated in the United States, Gusterov was influenced by the enthusiasm of a close business friend, Louis Vlasho, of Naples, Florida. The son of Macedonian immigrants and a 1959 graduate of Ohio University, Vlasho combined his own diversified career with serving as a consultant to Macedonian businesses. When Gusterov expressed a desire to help Macedonian students study abroad and return to become future leaders in their own country's move to a free-enterprise society, Vlasho encouraged him to examine his alma mater and its Cutler program. Gusterov did so and decided both offered values in which he had strong beliefs. Announcement of his decision to fund the scholarships was made at a press conference in Washington, D.C., attended by the donor, President Glidden, and U.S. Sen. George Voinovich (R-Ohio), former governor and Ohio University graduate with ancestral ties to the Macedonia region.

When three young women selected from eleven Macedonian schools as finalists for the first scholarship arrived at the campus for interviews, they were provided with housing at Claire Cottage. Bisera Gjosevska, who graduated from high school in the northern city of Kumanovo, was named winner. However, all three so impressed Cutler Scholar administrators and interviewers that philanthropist Gusterov decided to finance substantial scholarships for the other two as well. Bisera and her companions chose dual majors in finance and international business, and the lowest grade any of them received in her first quarter was one A minus in economics. To erase that from her record, she repeated the course, so each of the three completed her freshman year with a straight-A average.

One of Will's pleasures in continuing active participation at universities was the fulfillment of disclosing business vicissitudes encountered through experience to students about to launch their own careers. His personal philosophies, which modesty kept him from proffering unsolicited in conversations or even interviews, were better revealed when he was asked to meet with young people. In the fall of 2001, he accepted such an invitation to address a selected group of Ohio University engineering seniors and graduate students at an annual leadership institute created and conducted by Dean Emeritus Richard Robe. One purpose of the institute, described in its mission statement, was "to educate students about the fundamentals and the importance of effective leadership in professional practice in order to better serve the profession and society."

Drawing from more than half a century at the scientific business helm, he cautioned prospective leaders to "clearly communicate what a problem is and how you propose to solve it," then accept input from people who are going to help. "Often their ideas and insight are as good or better then yours," he said. "If they are performing the task daily, and have background and experience in the area, they most likely will be able to make constructive suggestions." It is important, he added, to acknowledge employees' roles in making things work, so they will realize it is their company, and they will share in its successes. "Be careful not to let your prejudice get in the way," he warned. "Being a scientist and engineer, for a time I felt the technical development of a company was the most important part of the business. I soon found you can have the best mouse trap, but if you don't have someone to market and sell it, you will go no place. I went from probably underpaying sales and marketing people to paying them more than I made as the owner of the company." To lower raised eyebrows, however, he confessed, "I caught up later."

To illustrate also that the leader of a business should convince employees that "they must turn out only the highest quality product and service, and realize the customer is king." Will described recent action by Diagnostic Hybrids following the September 11 tragedy in New York City:

> Because DHI viral diagnostic kits contain live cells, which are very fragile and short-lived, they are shipped by air. However, on September 12, the day bi-weekly shipments were due, all planes were grounded. So the company rented two trucks. President David Scholl and an employee headed south and east with one shipment, and two other employees drove north and west. The major chain laboratories have private aircrafts to pick up and deliver samples, so materials for their labs west of the Mississippi were flown by their own planes when limited air travel resumed on the thirteenth. DHI delivered that week's supplies to ninety percent of its customers. That's service, and all of the employees felt proud to be part of a group that went the extra mile to serve customers.

The plight of nuclear energy was a subject Will never initiated, but when pressed for an opinion, he did not hesitate to reveal strong feelings that seemed to represent those of most physicists who have knowledge and experience in that field. He believed America had "missed the boat badly" when it failed to follow up on its peaceful nuclear potential at the end of World War II. That mistake led not only to recurring worries about energy shortages but also to disastrous diplomatic struggles that were based, whether admittedly or not, on worldwide distribution of oil supplies. "I think we should have spent the money and time on research to make certain it was successful and safe, including the safe handling of the waste products from it, and I'm totally convinced that could have been done," he insisted.

A good beginning was made, and many nuclear engineering pioneers, including Arthur Compton, assumed it would lead to a new age of energy. In his highly regarded 1956 book, *Atomic Quest,* the man who played a key role in the Manhattan Project and became chancellor of Washington University in St. Louis, expressed a near certainty that atomic energy was "coming in just in time to meet a fundamental human need" and that it would, "to a very large extent," supplant coal and oil as the primary source of commercial heat and power. What he could not have envisioned at that time was the public outcry against nuclear energy, led by fiercely vocal opponents with high degrees of visibility and little or no knowledge of the subject. Some physicists attempted to refute the vacuous shouts, but most eventually withdrew from the hopeless debate to channel their research and development energies onto more promising paths. "The word spread that nuclear reactors were dangerous, so we just didn't spend the money to develop them," said Will. "Instead, we have spent billions of dollars on a political stance that in many ways has become warped to fit the need for importing oil. The way we deal with countries, even those with dictators, has been grossly influenced—probably necessarily—because of our reliance on foreign oil. If we had taken the technology that existed after World War II and poured the money and time into anything approaching what we did to build the bomb, we would have safe, cheap nuclear energy and would be able to handle the waste materials in a continuously safe manner. I just have no question in my mind about that."

Shipping waste from nuclear plants to sites for safe disposal became front-page issues in 2002, with debates often divided along political party lines. Agreeing that transporting radioactive materials holds a potential danger and must be handled with extreme caution, Will nevertheless likened it to other risks that have come to be accepted. "The world does not operate on zero tolerance," he said. "Don't cross a street because you might get hit. Don't allow gasoline trucks on the highways; we know of disastrous wrecks with them. Who would have thought men would deliberately fly airplanes into New York skyscrapers, killing thousands of people? You might make an argument—an obviously ridiculous one, to be sure—that such high towers should not have been built, for fear that they might become targets for terrorists."

Twenty-three years after the March 28, 1979, partial meltdown of a Three Mile Island nuclear power plant in Pennsylvania, many still cited that incident as a frightening reason for disapproval. Will agreed that the nation's only "semi-major problem" should not have happened, and although no life was lost, and "we ought to make certain it never happens again," it was not a horrible disaster. The major concern was that people in the area were subjected to radioactive iodine. With the progress of nuclear medicine, he explained, "we now feed patients more radioactive iodine to check their thyroid glands than any of the persons at Three Mile Island received. What happened there was terrible primarily because it scared people." (A class-action law suit representing 2,000 claims of personal health injury caused by gamma radiation exposure in the area of the nuclear plant went through district and appeals courts, all the way to the Supreme Court and back, for fifteen years before being dismissed, in favor of the defendants, in 1996.)

Although he acknowledged that talking about nuclear energy plants had become "politically incorrect," Will didn't completely forsake possibilities of their being resurrected, and indeed there was a hint of that coming about. It probably would be fifty more years before a "meaningful number of reactors" could be on line, he predicted, but he had not abandoned hope. "We have the technology and proof of their efficiency, and we can build in increasingly improved safety, both in operating reactors and in handling waste materials. This country has an entirely different technology and way of running plants, with far greater emphasis on safety, than was present at Chernobyl [referring to the 1986 explosion of a reactor at a power plant on the Pripyat' River in north-central Ukraine]."

In keeping with his general philosophy, Will believed education—in this instance for the general public—would be the most expedient method of revitalizing nuclear power production. That would require overcoming what he diagnosed as an epidemic of fear that had been stifling attempts to communicate meaningful information for half a century. He cited Chautauqua as an example of what can be done. Some presentations in the regular lecture series are designed to help educate people on current technologies, he said, "not in detail, but enough to provide sufficient understanding to counteract scare tactics. If enough people in the general public—in other words, the voters—had understood and agreed to build on our nuclear energy fifty years ago, we would have what we need today. I think the only way it is going to get turned around now is either we just plain run out of oil, or we get into an international situation where oil becomes so scarce, and therefore so expensive, that we have to go to some alternate system. I think wind power and solar panels and things like that are very good for certain specialized uses, but they aren't practical at this point for wide-scale power production." He did, however, foresee hope for the greatly increased production of hydrogen for use in automotive fuel cells—as long as the public isn't convinced to be alarmed by the fact that it is a highly explosive gas.

While Will continued his heavy philanthropic schedule into the new century, he still enjoyed the intrigue of expanding established sideline private business ventures and exploring prospects for new ideas. Success of fourteen Lion's Choice restaurants in the St. Louis area led to a board decision offering franchise opportunities to other investors. An article by Margie Manning in the June 6, 2000, *St. Louis Business Journal* reported: "Lion's Choice is roaring ahead with expansion plans, as the 33-year-old restaurant chain prepares to open its first franchise operations. Mark Disper likes the restaurant's signature roast beef sandwiches so much that he gave up a job in process management at Anheuser-Busch Companies to buy the first franchise. It will open in early June in suburban Chicago (Warrenville)." A second franchise followed, opened by St. Louis–based Drury Development Company at the Mississippi River historic port city of Cape Girardeau in southeastern Missouri.

Although Lion's Choice had achieved excellent name recognition in St. Louis, a fifteenth company-owned restaurant was struggling in Kansas City. Will and his co-owners, realizing the difficulty of financing adequate media advertising for a single operation, in contrast to a joint effort for fourteen in one area, recommended that prospective franchise groups consider a chain. As a result, a group of St. Louis investors purchased ten franchise rights, with restaurants starting at the edge of the city and extending over a period of time to Columbia, Jefferson City, Springfield, and Kansas City. Early in 2002, the growth of interest being shown by other prospective groups was such that Lion's Choice set up a separate franchise phase of its operations. At the same time, it looked further beyond its traditional business boundaries toward possible locations at malls and designing new buildings to emphasize what Will described as fast-food service with the relaxed aura of a regular restaurant. The lean roast beef and other items on an extensive menu, as well as cooking methods, placed a premium on health consciousness. Although he was not involved in day-to-day activities, Will was active and influential on the board, as he had been since joining the three founders to expand from a single suburban restaurant in the late 1960s.

Will seemed always to enjoy backing new inventors in an assortment of technologies and with varying degrees of success. One of his favorites in the early months of 2002 was initiated by a radiologist whose fascination with computers led him to create a program for doctor's offices. If successful, physicians would be able to enter notes and patient histories directly into a computer and even do the billing on the same program. All such data would be stored on the Internet, with an individual access code for each patient. Wherever the patient might be, obtaining permission and the code from the patient's doctor would enable another physician to call up all pertinent information needed to help with diagnosis and treatment. Helping arrange to test the program through a number of physicians, Will assumed there would be early glitches but gave it a good chance to become a business that could be built up or sold.

Some projects he rated high in concepts but found to be low in developer ability or integrity were shunted aside before they could become substantial drains on venture capital. In his opinion, these were mere speed bumps in the paths to uncharted destinations. Like other explorers, he never tired of the search, and both friends and colleagues time after time expressed wonder at his high batting average. His own response was low key: "I have a lot of interests and I like to keep moving."

He showed extreme interest in advanced diagnostic imaging research being carried out by radiologists at Washington University's School of Medicine, where members of the Department of Radiology were digitizing X rays and storing them on CDs, to be pulled up on computers in most parts of the world. He also remained active in the ongoing Athenian II venture capital effort in Athens, which had reached $32 million and was still growing steadily.

Triannual meetings of the Ohio University Foundation Board ordinarily were held on the campus. However, the first session of 2002 took place February 15–16 at New York City, thanks to special arrangements made by Richard Wilhelm, a former president and general manager of the city's Plaza Hotel. Will and Ann Lee planned their trip to combine the business sessions with a weekend of attending two plays and a ballet. What they did not expect was an addendum to the agenda that took place after a Friday night dinner. With Will's eightieth birthday just five days away, board representatives of the foundation celebrated this milestone anniversary by presenting its only lifetime trustee with a plaque honoring his long service to Ohio University. Conferred by Ohio University President Glidden, it read:

> We celebrate you for decades of dedication to Alma Mater. You have given your time, your energies, your philanthropic resources, and your considerable good counsel to Ohio University's success.
>
> You are the quintessential exemplar of "loyal volunteer." You have served on boards and committees, as chairman of the 1804 Campaign, and co-chairman of The Third Century Campaign, and sit on the Executive Committee of the Bicentennial Campaign Cabinet.
>
> Your vision and inspiration helped create the unique Cutler Scholars Program and you co-founded and continue to nurture the highly successful Diagnostic Hybrids, Inc.
>
> On a personal level, we revere you as a gentleman and as a gentle man, one who always has time for Alma Mater, is gracious in giving of his time and expertise, and sets a remarkable standard to which all who love Ohio University should aspire.

16

VINTAGE KONNEKER

A great secret of success is to go through life as
a man who never gets used up.
— ALBERT SCHWEITZER

On February 20, 2002, the eightieth birthday of Will Konneker, a coterie of St. Louis friends gathered for a surprise party arranged by Ann Lee and their daughter, B. Lynn Webster. Although it was not as elaborate as the golden wedding event, timing again was important, so the honoree would be absent when guests arrived, but home before five o'clock. Charlie Ping had telephoned from Athens, Ohio, to ask if Ann Lee could "guarantee having her husband home at that precise hour to receive an important birthday present." Fortunately, Will, with no intention of considering it a special day, was scheduled to attend an all-afternoon meeting of the Lion's Choice board. By contacting the board chairman, secretary Sue Winter made arrangements to have the meeting concluded in a manner that would assure Will's return home within a specified period of time. The plan worked to perfection, said Ann Lee, even though she became ill and had to remain in her bedroom while B. Lynn took over cooking responsibilities and greeted the guests. Everything was in place when a much-surprised Dr. K opened the door from his garage, right on schedule. Then, while the group began to enjoy appetizers and conversations, Will was called to the telephone by his daughter. When he put the receiver to his ear, he heard a greeting from Dr. Ping, followed by a special chorus of student voices singing "Happy Birthday." The former Ohio University president somehow had assembled the entire group of Cutler Scholars on campus for the musical message. "It was the finest present I could have received," said a deeply moved Will Konneker. The incident was reminiscent of an observation once made by Jack Ellis: "I have never met anyone who is so sincerely touched by acts of kindness as Will."

Knowing that Will also appreciated interesting bits of trivia, in particular those centered on numbers, one of the guests interrupted festivities at two minutes past eight o'clock to make "an historic announcement" arranged by Sue Winter. Assuming that guests were acquainted with military time designations, he proclaimed, "This incredible Konneker birthday moment is exactly 2002, 2002, 2002. Eight o'clock being a military twenty, we are celebrating at two minutes past twenty on the twentieth day of the second month of the year two thousand and two. A phenomenon equal to that hasn't occurred previously for a thousand and one years, when someone must have celebrated a birthday at one minute after ten on the first day of October in the year 1001, and it will never happen again, because there can't be a thirtieth hour of the day."

Conversations focused more on current city and world concerns than the nostalgia that might be expected on such an occasion. Those who knew Will and Ann Lee Konneker intimately understood the unlikelihood of directing topics to the past when so many new ideas were in motion. As their fifty-seventh wedding anniversary approached, Will and his wife still were delving into philanthropic, business, educational, and arts projects with uncommon vitality.

Will's full head of hair, now white, still was wavy. His shoulders had not the least hint of a slouch, and his affinity for brisk walking enabled him to keep fit without a structured exercise regimen. At a cocktail party not attended by the Konnekers, Will's reputation for natty attire led to a friendly accusation that his clothes surely must have been selected by Ann Lee, known for always being exquisitely yet tastefully dressed. "What difference does it make?" responded Joan Wood, a longtime friend who had served with Will on the Ohio University Foundation Board, "they nearly always think alike." Others in the group nodded their agreement.

A reluctance to reminisce in great detail, unless gently prodded by a persistent inquisitor, detracted not at all from their appreciation of days gone by. Quite the contrary. Witness the hometown scholarships, Ann Lee's regular summer luncheons with high school classmates during Chautauqua seasons, and the scores of lasting friendships they cherished beyond all other attainments. They accumulated relationships, with a remarkable number remaining current through the years—updated by meetings, visits, and correspondence. Entire families of the "Bridgers" group spent weekends together at Missouri's Tan-Tar-A resort on the Lake of the Ozarks. "Nearly all of those who have been their closest friends through the years have made trips with them at one time or another," said Elmer Boehm.

Mixed with each day's typical glut of throwaway mail were regular personal letters from university administrators, faculty members, past and present colleagues on diversified committees and boards, former Mallinckrodt overseas associates, traveling companions, lifelong chums, and even youthful e-mail-oriented Cutler Scholars who took the time to write.

When pressured to reflect on incidents in his life, Will would acknowledge the possibility of some specific influences by teachers, friends, and others, but his analytical mind was reluctant to accept the intriguing correlations feature writers and broadcasters are wont to dramatize. "I did things because that is how I felt, not because someone convinced me, consciously or subconsciously, to do them," he said. "I don't like to draw conclusions on assumptions, no matter how logical they might appear, because they generally are not based on hard evidence."

He was prone to squelch, probably correctly, any imagined gene-related link between his entrepreneurial bent and that of his father. Coincidental as it might be, however, it was apparent that the elder Konneker had been no ordinary haircutter. After expanding his diverse interests into multiple barbershops, real estate sales, and contracting in Detroit, he retired temporarily to Miami Shores, Florida, where he bought a home. Because he didn't like hot weather, however, he and his wife, Ruth, returned each summer to Detroit, where Roy continued to buy, improve, and sell buildings. He was an expert carpenter, even able to do finished work.

Roy seemed always to provide surprises. No one in the family knew he could speak fluent German until Ruth and their daughter, Karen, heard him carrying on an animated conversation in that language with a group of immigrants from his ancestral country. In later life, he confessed to having chosen his son's middle name, not because of its German flavor but for its popularity associated with Hollywood's leading motion picture star, Rudolph Valentino, who actually had been born Rodolfo Alfonzo Raffaelo Pierre Filibert Guglielmi di Valentina D'Antonguolla, in Castellaneta, Italy. Roy also enjoyed the noncoincidence of Will and his sister, Winona Rosalie Konneker, sharing the same initials. Ann Lee's favorite story about her father-in-law related to his cooking: "He loved to fix German potato salad, and it was delicious, but he had only one recipe, which started out with a peck of potatoes. That meant he had to put in proportionate amounts of onions, hard-boiled eggs, spices, vinegar, mayonnaise, diced bacon, and pickles. It was enough for an army battalion."

Less than two weeks after Will's eightieth birthday, his sister, Winona Conley, died at the age of eighty-three in Tallahassee, where she lived with her son, Donald Long, his wife, Carolyn, and their son, Konner. The fact that she had been in failing health for two years did little to lessen the sadness in losing the person who had suffered with him through the desolation of early life in a sanatorium, helped buttress his changeover to a happy childhood, and championed the successes of his career. Winona was buried at Akron, Ohio, where she had been an inner-city elementary school teacher for ten years, met and married Charles Long, an aircraft industrial designer, and reared two sons, Donald and David. Charles died in 1970, and four years later Winona married Ray Conley, remaining in Akron for twelve more years until he died in 1986. In 1988, she moved to Fort Lauderdale, Florida, to live less than a mile from Donald and his wife, sharing a condominium with Carolyn's mother for six years. She then moved in with Don and Carolyn, remaining with them when they later moved to Tallahassee. A 1973 graduate of the University of Akron, with a master's degree from George Washington University, Don attended evening and weekend classes to receive a Ph.D. in public administration from Florida Atlantic University. Both he and his wife, who held a B.A. degree in English from Florida Atlantic, were public management consultants in Tallahassee. "Even though Winona had grown frail and was not in good health, her passing was a shock to us all," Carolyn said. "It was a great loss for Konner. His grandmother was an everyday part of his life. They were great pals."

David Long, a 1969 graduate of the University of Akron, was with Mutual of America, the New York–based life insurance company. A second vice president in the Akron regional field office, which covered most of Ohio, he was in charge of administrating both company and individual retirement plans. He and his wife, Patricia, were married the weekend of her June graduation from the University of Akron in 1970. She taught school for five years, before becoming a full-time homemaker, while David pursued his insurance career, first with Equitable, then, since 1981, with Mutual. They had three children, Kimberly, Nancy, and Brian. Nancy graduated summa cum laude in finance from Ohio University in 1998, and two years later she married Todd Neville.

Both David and Donald had fond childhood memories of visiting Granddad Konneker in Detroit, remembering in particular his sense of humor and how he massaged their heads and backs with an electric hand-held vibrator when he gave them haircuts. "I also enjoy recalling how we all tried to get coconuts off the palm trees when we visited Granddad Roy and Ruth in Florida," Don said.

Ruth Konneker, Roy's widow, continued to live in the Detroit suburb of Westland. Her daughter, Karen Lafferty, a half-sister of Will and Winona, also lived in that city, with her husband, Wayne, and their teenage son, Marc. Karen also had a son and daughter from a previous marriage, both of them married and living in Colorado.

Ann Lee and her sister, Jane Edwards, greatly enjoyed getting together as often as possible, just as they had on weekends when they were at separate universities. Although they seldom were described as lookalikes, it was not difficult to recognize them as being siblings. At five-feet-four, Ann Lee was slightly shorter than Jane, and they shared a special fondness for spontaneous humor. Many friends noted that their telephone voices were indistinguishable. Jane, who had been the more athletic of the two, also tended to be more structured in her lifestyle. Ann Lee continued the free-spirit mannerism she had shown in her youth. Jean Hope, whose long friendship extended back to the late forties when she came to the United States from Scotland, described her as "an original": "That's one of the things that makes Ann Lee so special to me. She can be counted on to defend her own position. She doesn't go with the crowd unless it is an opinion she happens to share. And Will obviously likes that spirit. I wouldn't go so far as to say they always agree with each other, but rather, their personalities complement each other. That's why they can be much different as individuals but definitely a great match."

In 2002, Jane still spent winters in Bradenton, Florida, and summers at Chautauqua. Her son, Jeffrey, a geologist, was pursuing his profession in various parts of the western United States and South America. Jeff and his cousin, B. Lynn, became special friends in 1970, when he and his mother spent a year with her father in the house on the Konneker property near Ellisville. "It was like having a big brother," B. Lynn recalled. "I loved it."

Asked to reflect on the decision fifty-two years earlier to form a company in an unknown field, right out of college, Will and Ann Lee disclaimed any suggestion of having been apprehensive, explaining that they just decided to give it a try and see what would happen. "We didn't have anything, so we didn't have a great deal to lose," Ann Lee recalled. Will added that he and his partner, Ken Morganstern, believed they had a good idea and had decent assurance of doing business with Jewish Hospital. "We believed that would be our first bread-and-butter account," he remembered, "and although it wouldn't even buy the bread today, it could buy a little of that, and some butter, in 1950."

After the two founders parted when Will bought the company back from its brief merger with Nuclear Corporation of America in 1958, they didn't correspond for several years. While Will was building his career, Radiation Dynamics, the New York company that evolved from Telray, also flourished under the supervision of Morganstern and Marshall Cleland, becoming the world's leader in the manufacture of industrial electron beam accelerators. So the young men who were doctoral students together at Washington University, launched a company together, and later followed separate routes to success were virtually out of touch until 1984, when Will contacted Ken for participation in the scholarship campaign to honor their former teacher, Dr. Hughes. Nine years later, they became further reacquainted when Ken telephoned his former partner after reading a featured article about the Konnekers in the university's publication, *My Washington*. After that, the two men talked occasionally by telephone and exchanged Christmas messages. Morganstern, who had a large family, retired in the nineties, and his wife died soon afterward. An interesting sidelight to the early Konneker-Morganstern connection began with Ken meeting a Washington University coed who later became his wife. She moved to New York City following graduation, and her presence there proved to be an enticement for him to leave St. Louis and start the first Nuclear Consultants branch laboratory, which in turn led to the series of events shaping the careers of both men. It was the kind of retrospective sequence that typifies patterns of most lives, perhaps engaging simply for that reason.

When describing complex processes or equipment relating to nuclear physics, Will often liked to sketch detailed illustrations as he spoke. "Sometimes, that seems to be the only way I can convert esoteric thinking into layman's language," he said. Surprisingly, the procedure worked well. For example, with his pencil swooping around an eight-and-a-half-inch paper pad in sync with his words, he actually could guide a nonscientific mind, at least momentarily, through the early development of a simulation counter from this description: "We found that if we took a piece of crystal—in fact, the very first one was a mothball—and let a gamma ray hit it, the interaction would produce a little faint flash of light. But what the hell do you do with a little flash of light? You can't see it with your naked eye. But this sees it, because the light strikes a photosensitive thing plated onto the inside of this tube [pause to draw the tube], and knocks off an electron. What you have done is put a series of plates in here and so an electron hits this and two of them come off, perhaps, and are drawn over this one. This happens instantaneously. Then it goes to this one and bounces to this one, and every time it goes, it produces more electrons, and then this goes out into this. And now we have a pulse of electricity going into this, which is a counter. Each time one of these comes through, it is counted. So you can see how this is about ten times more efficient than a Geiger Counter [which he also draws and simultaneously explains for clarification]."

Since its beginning in 1876, the St. Louis Zoo grew to become known as one of the finest in the country. Guided by a succession of civic leaders, and the first to be supported by city government, it expanded steadily to occupy seventy acres in Forest Park. Open throughout the year, and free of charge to the public, it gained renown for its zoological collections, educational programs, and dedication to conserving endangered species. The people of St. Louis seemed to take great pride in their zoo and were willing to help in furthering its success. Even schoolchildren contributed money to purchase an elephant. In the latter part of the twentieth century, having established its reputation as a standard zoo, it became a leader in moving animals from cages into exterior areas resembling their natural habitats. Trails and a narrow-gauge railroad led through outdoor complexes with names such as "Big Cat Country" and, more recently, "River's Edge."

To increase this phase of its development, the zoo launched a "Gateway to the Animal World" capital fund campaign, scheduled to be completed in 2004. When Will and Ann Lee made an early major gift to the drive, they did not realize the size of their contribution would result in special recognition. Beginning in 2002, however, visitors could follow the "Konneker Hippo Trail," appropriately identified by a plaque, to a River's Edge immersion exhibit and watch the massive African *Hippopotamus amphibius* float under water, before moving on to see a variety of other animals from around the world in their natural environments.

Will and Ann Lee also provided generous financial support to the St. Louis Science Center, which was dedicated to helping children and adults understand interrelationships of technology, people, and the environment. "It does a good job of educating young people and, in fact, the general public through awareness of technology," Will said, "not to make scientists out of them, but to offer them background knowledge through displays and projects geared to various age groups." An overall goal of the center, expressed in its statement of purpose, was to "meet society's needs for scientific literacy." As patrons, the Konnekers regularly attended openings of various programs.

In 1993, Will and Ann Lee, Charlie and Claire Ping, and Kenner and Margene Bush spent several days together in London. By design, they were met there by Samuel Crowl, an Ohio University trustee professor of English spending a sabbatical studying and writing on his special field of interest, Shakespeare and Renaissance drama. With them, and also on a sabbatical, was Susan Crowl, who, like her husband, was an Ohio University professor of English. The Konnekers had known Sam Crowl for many years, first when he spoke to wives of fund board members, and next when he accepted an invitation to speak on his favorite topic, Shakespeare, at a St. Louis Alumni Chapter party in the country home near Ellisville (where he recalled "admiring the old home they had very much made their own and being introduced to some Doberman pinschers"). Eight years later, the Konnekers and Pings enjoyed a rerun visit to the English capital, spending another week with the Crowls, who again were on sabbaticals. During the interim, they were together on occasions drawing the Konnekers to the campus. From those close associations, Dr. Crowl, who also served for a time as a university dean, reflected on what he observed of their personalities:

They do love to go to the opera and theater and symphony. These things, of course, have been of major importance to Ann Lee most of her life (she majored in English Literature at Ohio State), and I can tell that Will also enjoys good theater and good music. That is genuine. He always has something pertinent to say about what we have seen together, and he has a good memory for what he has seen and heard in the past. And they are one of those wonderful couples who seem to enjoy both themselves and others in what they do together.

Sam Crowl was among the many close friends who had favorite Rolls Royce anecdotes concerning Will's treasured vehicle. "I remember that on one of their trips to Athens, when they brought B. Lynn along, Susan and I invited them to our house on Boyd Street," he said. "It was a lovely June evening, and as they wheeled up in front of our house, I told myself that there probably weren't many Shakespeare professors in the world who would be visited on their tiny streets by friends in Rolls Royces. Will and Ann Lee, of course, wouldn't even have such a thought, because they don't have an ounce of pretension between them. When they're in London, they enjoy the small fringe theaters as much as the Royal National Theater." Crowl offered the thought that Will "admires Britain and at least what we used to think of as British quality" as one possible factor in his attraction to the Rolls Royce.

Claire Ping enjoyed reflecting on times she saw Will and Ann Lee drive into the parking lot of the alumni center with the backseat of their Rolls Royce loaded like the back of a pickup truck with furniture, and on other occasions when they arrived with a heavy five-foot David Hostetler sculpture. The wood sculpture, "Pony Tail," one in the American Woman series by the eminent Ohio University sculptor/professor, had been placed on loan in the president's home and become a favorite of Mrs. Ping. Seeing it there, Ann Lee expressed such admiration for the work that Will surprised her by purchasing it for their St. Louis home. Afterward, however, he learned that Claire had become so attached to it that she truthfully missed having it in her own living room. Consequently, Will wrapped the sculpture and transported it to and from Athens—on the Rolls Royce backseat, of course—on several trips to the university.

Having never thought about reasons and, in fact, being unaware of friends' conjectures, Will nevertheless concurred that he valued good machinery, especially in the form of a vehicle, and was willing to contribute, for the record, how he happened to become a Rolls devotee. He had, indeed, admired the English automobile for some time and was curious about its special features, but there was no dealer in St. Louis, so he had not given ownership a serious thought until he attended a 1982 convention of the Nuclear Medicine Society in Palm Beach, Florida. Noticing that the city had a large Rolls Royce dealership, he wandered from the hotel during an afternoon of meetings in which he had no particular interest to look over the cars. "I liked them, of course," he remembered, "so I discussed them with dealers, then went back to the meetings." The following day, he returned to look at the cars more closely, make a deal, telephone his banker to wire money, and drive back to the hotel in his first Rolls. When the conference was concluded, he drove to Chautauqua, where he and an unsuspecting Ann Lee were staying for their brief summer respite. Before arriving at the house, he telephoned his wife with a report of the purchase: "I have a new toy and I'm sure you will like it because it drove beautifully all the way from Palm Springs, and it stopped at every gas station." He bought his second Rolls Royce at Wichita, Kansas, in 1988, and its successor at Dublin, Ohio, in 1998 (during a visit to the home of his longtime, boyhood friend, Ed Hope). St. Louis still did not have a dealership.

As their friendships deepened, the Konnekers and Pings made regular overseas vacation excursions together. In addition to the London trips, they went to Japan, Singapore, Italy, Wales, Taiwan, Greece, the Greek islands, and South Africa, the latter while Ping was on the Fulbright assignment to Namibia. Although they toured South Africa's wine country, took the Blue Train to Victoria Falls in Zimbabwe, and enjoyed fascinating attractions of Cape Town, the most lasting impression came from being stuck in the African bush on the way to a wildlife preserve in Namibia. Having learned the territory during his work in Namibia, Charlie Ping was the designated automobile driver as the four friends headed across a desolate area on a narrow road that had what Will described as "major dips that filled up with sand." As they approached one particularly large such obstacle, Charlie advised his passengers, "Hang on, and our momentum will carry us right through this thing." Instead, the vehicle sank in—up to the frame. With nothing but barren land in sight, the emeritus university president and the nuclear physicist began digging into the sand, with faint hope of freeing the car, but with no apparent alternative. Just when the effort seemed hopeless, however, a man on a tractor suddenly appeared, seemingly out of nowhere but probably from behind a clump of trees. After pulling the car from the sand and being properly rewarded, he just as mysteriously disappeared. Although they were forever grateful for his fateful arrival on the scene, they always questioned how he happened to be right there in the middle of nowhere with a tractor, within view of the largest sand-filled dip in the road they encountered during the entire trip.

"Our friendship with Will and Ann Lee developed so naturally and spontaneously that I can't really trace it back to any specific instance," Charlie Ping said. "I think right from the start we enjoyed each other and shared a lot of interests." Claire Ping remembered that there was "an interesting connection" long before they knew each other. While her husband was working toward his Ph.D. at Duke University, Claire was employed as the administrative assistant to the chairman of the Department of Biochemistry from 1955 to 1958. "Our graduate research students used radioisotopes, and I remember vividly that the only place we could get them was from Will's company in St. Louis."

Lighter moments in the lives of Will and Ann Lee, recalled often by close friends, served to counterbalance the no-nonsense degree of intensity that might be attributed to a career encompassing nuclear medicine, entrepreneurship, and philanthropy. On one of their trips to Australia, Will and Ann Lee purchased a didgeridoo, the ingenious Aboriginal wind instrument made from a tree branch that has been naturally hollowed out by termites. The six-foot-long instrument, curved to rest on the floor while being played, would be a perfect fit for Mel Dodd, their lanky friend from Wichita, they reasoned, so they had it shipped to him as a gift. They also sent him a book with music and instructions on the difficult technique of playing the didgeridoo by expelling air from the cheeks while breathing in through the nose. Despite that complexity, Mel learned it well enough to give a surprise performance at the Konnekers' golden wedding anniversary, in a barely distinguishable rendition of "The Anniversary Waltz." In 2000, Will and Ann Lee greatly mourned Mel's death from ALS (Lou Gehrig's Disease), and continued their close relationship with his wife, Millie.

In 1973, the year Will left his full-time association with Mallinckrodt in favor of half-time consulting, he thought it would be a good idea for the family to experience skiing. Plans to attend Denver meetings of the Society of Nuclear Medicine offered the ideal opportunity, because they would be held a week before eighth-grader B. Lynn's spring break. Arrangements were made, and at the conclusion of the meetings, Ann Lee and their daughter flew to Denver; then, all three took a bus to Winter Park Resort. None of the three had been on skies, so Will hired instructors to get them started. What happened next became a scenario kept alive through the years by friends' demands for reruns. Ann Lee described how her husband, while struggling to follow the instructor's advice, somehow started going down the slope backward, until his inevitable crash. He, in turn, remembered his wife's experience with a stern German instructor. The first time she fell, and was having difficulty getting upright, the instructor demanded, "You vill get up." Returning his forceful scowl and duplicating his assertive tone, Ann Lee replied, "I vill not!" Instead, she removed her skis and never got on them again. Will, however, learned to negotiate the intermediate slopes, and B. Lynn became an enthusiastic skier. Later all three went with friends to Vail, Aspen, Breckenridge, and other ski resorts, but only father and daughter took to the slopes. Bill Webster, in addition to being an accomplished horseman, was a certified ski instructor, so he, B. Lynn, and their children, Cara and Trey, spent many winter weekends at Hidden Valley in the Wildwood suburb of St. Louis, and at other ski areas.

Will never objected to being the target for humorous portrayals and, in fact, sometimes told tales on himself. An example was his confession to being somewhat less than competent in the art of sailing. He had no particular desire to participate in that sport, but after purchasing the summer home at Chautauqua, he thought it only appropriate to get a small sailboat that B. Lynn could enjoy on the beautiful big lake that was just a few hundred yards away. He bought a Butterfly, the popular twelve-foot, one-sail, swamp-proof craft with an airtight sealed hull that guaranteed it to be unsinkable. Advertisements exclaimed that it was light enough to be launched by one person and fast enough for competition, and that if it capsized, it could be popped back up easily. Its stability and ease of handling made it ideal for a young beginning sailor. The claims were true enough, but B. Lynn wasn't as attracted to sailing as she was to horseback riding and skiing, and when she entered college, she wasn't able to visit Chautauqua very often. As a result, the boat seldom was used. "Rather than see it just sit there, I decided I might as well use it," Will recalled. "Well, I got along pretty well, and even on some pretty windy occasions when I flipped it over on its side, I was able to get it back up, just as the ads said. Then one day I turtled it—all the way over with the mast straight down in the water. That was a more difficult problem, and I was struggling, pretty much in vain, when I heard a young voice ask, 'Can we help you, mister?' And along came two little girls who swam over and flipped the boat right back up. I sold it the next day."

A compelling curiosity to explore new ventures led Will to active participation in endeavors more often consigned to armchair musing and cocktail party pipe dreaming. Whereas most men were content with a "what-if" conclusion, Will needed to find out. Nuclear Consultants, of course, was the most vivid example. But consider also racquetball courts, race horses, Lion's Choice, Telray, Infa-Care, and the others. Friends admired both his daring and his high percentage of demonstrating a Midas touch, and they were right. Yet the attempt in itself was necessary for his personal fulfillment. Not having tried would haunt him to the extent that he didn't suffer from, nor feel a compulsion to whitewash a rare loser. Au contraire, it could even become something he and Ann Lee would laugh about in later years:

Just by happenstance, the Konnekers discovered a small St. Louis restaurant that served what they considered the best fried chicken they had tasted. Operated by an elderly owner, his wife, and a cook, Missouri Fried Chicken was "not much to look at, but an excellent place to eat," in Ann Lee's judgment. As time went by, they discovered the same opinion was held by John Jarvis, Will's colleague before and after his merger into Mallinckrodt and in the racquetball business (the same man who later joined Diagnostic Hybrids in Athens). When the owner decided to retire, Jarvis suggested that they buy special recipes that had been carefully guarded, hire the cook, pay the outgoing proprietor to be a consultant, and build another Missouri Fried Chicken restaurant in a better section of the city. Will liked the idea, so he and Jarvis, who was to operate the business, became partners, moved the restaurant to its new location, and opened with an inaugural dinner attended by invited friends. Will and Ann Lee had to be away on the night of the grand opening, but when they returned, they learned it had been less than grand. A mistake in delivery of the equipment had resulted in installation of a solid-plate stove resembling a huge grill, without individual burners, that completely befuddled the cook. By the time she figured out how to use it, the long-suffering guests were tired of waiting. Unfortunately, the experience proved to be a harbinger of MFC's fate. The cook, who had played a vital role in the old restaurant, was unable to adjust, even after the stove was replaced, and her former employer gave up his consulting. With all his other responsibilities, Will was unable to get involved in daily concerns, and Jarvis, despite a valiant effort, shared with Will the problem of "very limited knowledge of restaurateuring," while a "procession of chefs" passed through the kitchen. "If we had been able to keep the original cook and gotten more advice from the old gentleman, we probably could have made it," said Will, "but we kept trying for about a year, then got out of it." He concluded that, "The only way to be successful in the restaurant business, unless you are exceptionally lucky, is to make it a family affair and be there." Without regret, he said emphatically, "Something like Lion's Choice, fine. A full restaurant, no way."

On the subject of food, Hiroshi Ogawa maintained that Will's "challenging spirit and interests" were not confined to business. "Whenever we were together in my country, he tried various Japanese foods that most foreign people hesitate to eat," Dr. Ogawa said. "For instance, he ate mud fish, which is similar to eel and a popular Japanese food. Among my many foreign friends, there are only two persons who eat mud fish, and Will is one of them." Recalling other examples, Dr. Ogawa jokingly related a time when Will ate raw horse meat, a delicacy in some areas of Japan. "It tastes much like tuna fish," the Japanese scientist said, "and he, in fact, thought it *was* tuna. After I told him it was horse meat, he reminded me of his daughter's love of horses and asked me not to tell B. Lynn what he had just eaten, or she might kill him." Dick Yoshida added that both Will and Ann Lee also liked to try such things as "miso soup, grilled dried fishes, seaweed, and Japanese-style pickles with rice, popular in different districts of the country."

In 2002, the twenty-fifth anniversary of Sue Winter's association with Will Konneker, first as Racquetball Courts secretary and most recently as his assistant in Konneker Development Corporation, her employer stated, "I haven't written a paycheck for her in ten years." She seemed to have total recall of everything that took place and could provide almost instantaneous answers to questions concerning names, dates, places, costs, business associates, friends, family, meetings, and telephone numbers. Contacting her by e-mail was certain to bring a rapid reply. Will's remark about the paycheck was no exaggeration. The attractive executive secretary handled bookkeeping and wrote all checks, whether or not the man she always referred to as "Dr. K" was in town. Their rapport was obvious to persons who dealt with Konneker Development in person or by telephone. She was one of the closest friends of Will, Ann Lee, and B. Lynn. The family Doberman, Trudy, who appeared in many ways to have human instincts, welcomed her as part of the clan. (Sue and her husband, Gary, who met in high school, were married when she was nineteen, a year before she began working with Konneker Development. They had two children, Patrick and Cara.)

When Will Konneker left his full-time position at Mallinckrodt, a retired business friend predicted, "What you will miss most are a copy machine and a secretary." Still warming to the memory of those words nearly three decades later, Will noted smilingly, "I wisely decided I wasn't going to suffer such a plight. I've never been without a copy machine since that time, and I can't imagine running Konneker Development without Sue."

Visitors to his Manchester office in 2002 were struck by the manner in which he operated as a one-man private foundation. Hardly could he have worked more diligently in gaining substantial wealth than he did in giving it away and encouraging others to do likewise. One of the distinguishing characteristics of Will was his self-motivated philanthropy. Fundraisers agreed that most donors responded only to appeals. Will did that, but he also took the initiative to identify worthwhile causes and beneficiaries on his own. He recognized the insatiable financial needs of education at many levels, including public enlightenment, and vigorously recruited others to join him in that type of support. Family, friends, and persons who joined him in such efforts shook their heads in astonishment at the way he maintained his energy and enthusiasm day after day, year after year, without retreating from what he considered obligations to society.

Away from his office, he maintained the same pace. After a day's sessions at a gathering of the Ohio University Foundation Board, a much younger Bob Axline commented on keeping up with Will, "I started with him at seven thirty in the morning, and we rushed from one meeting to another in various rooms of the University Inn—all on entrepreneurial subjects—until five thirty that afternoon, taking lunch on the fly, yet he didn't even seem to tire."

Will claimed that he owed much to many. In truth, his life was one of primarily making his own way. Always with his wife at his side, he exuded what Jack Ellis detected as a discernible confidence without shedding an ounce of humility. "Ann Lee and Will complement one another," Ellis said. "They obviously enjoy being together, but they keep each other humble. They joust and spar with each other with comments that keep their feet on the ground, because they both have done pretty remarkable things in their lives. They play against each other in a dramatic, but nice way that keeps their sense of perspective. They have a lot of fun doing this, and I think they enjoy pricking one another's balloon if they think anything is getting a little overplayed."

Washington University Vice Chancellor Blassingame spoke for many other good friends and business associates in describing the Konnekers as "warm people who have built a lot of friends over the years," in the St. Louis community as well as universities and elsewhere. "They have a sincere and gracious way of doing things, so everyone really enjoys being with them," he said.

During his career, Will worked successfully at overcoming a natural degree of shyness, something that never posed a problem for Ann Lee. He became comfortable in diversified social situations, from diplomatic gatherings to the Pumpkin Show at Chillicothe. Having not attended the latter since his teenage years in nearby Greenfield, he accepted an invitation from Chillicothe-native Ellis to attend the annual event in the late nineties. Ellis remembered it well:

> Will was wearing an elegant ultra-suede coat as we walked
> around, enjoying the festival. When we came to a concession
> stand selling sugar waffles, the kind they deep fry with batter
> and cover with confectioner sugar, he stopped and said, "I
> haven't had one of those since I was a kid, but I sure loved them
> then." So he ordered one, and on the first bite it fell apart,
> spraying his coat with powdered sugar. Well, he broke out in
> that close-mouthed smile of his, making it obvious that he re-

ally enjoyed it. He was reliving a moment from his youth, and he couldn't have cared less about what happened to the front of his coat.

When Will made his annual pilgrimage to Greenfield for the presentation of the 2002 Konneker Cutler Scholarship at McClain High School's June commencement, he was accompanied by close friend Jack Pirozzi, who had visited the town twenty-five years earlier and remembered being intrigued by several of its historic homes and churches. Pirozzi was afraid the long-planned excursion would be canceled when Will began to experience difficulty with a knee, but Will, twenty-five years his senior, insisted not only that he could manage the trip but also that it be extended a day to also visit Ohio University. Flying to Columbus, then driving to Athens, Will provided what his much younger friend described as "a whirlwind tour of the campus and town":

We arrived by mid-afternoon on June 7 and proceeded to visit entrepreneurial sites for business development, classroom buildings, the Konneker Alumni Center, the sports facilities, the Galbreath Chapel, the Kennedy Museum, Cutler Hall, and other places that meant so much to him. Throughout the day, Will's mood was positive and upbeat, and not once did he complain of what I'm sure was an uncomfortable knee. His obvious pride in Ohio University seemed to buoy his spirits and his exuberance, and I noticed that such enthusiasm was infectious. Wherever we went, he was greeted and welcomed warmly, and it was obvious that he was genuinely touched by the recognition. By evening, I was ready for a quiet dinner and assumed Will would welcome a chance to rest his knee. Instead, he was ready for us to head for a Symposiarc cookout, as guests of Jack Ellis. I learned that the organization was made up of men associated with both the university and the city and was being hosted by a leading businessman, Harold Laughlin, at his country home. So we spent an enjoyable three or four hours greeting old friends and former colleagues before returning to the Ohio University Inn at ten o'clock. The next morning, we headed across the eighty miles of rolling hill country to Greenfield.

Along the way, Will told about the many times he had hitch-hiked those roads when money was scarce and there was no public transportation between the two towns. When I asked him if he always was able to get a ride, he replied, "I never remember walking very long."

Sight-seeing in Will's hometown proved to be no less exhaustive. The two men motored through business and residential areas Will once covered on his bicycles, looking at the majestic old cut-limestone mansions on a still tree-lined Second Street, pausing in front of McClain High School, and stopping to view the modest Konneker family home on Jefferson Street. Will remarked that he had "spent many an hour in the large backyard tending to Aunt Olive's vegetable garden," and while he wasn't particularly pleased with being assigned to that work, he recognized its importance. "We took care of ourselves then," he told his companion. "It was among my most important first lessons."

North of town, Will and Jack visited a cemetery where several Konneker family members were buried. Noticing that a few headstones were askew, Will drove to Hardy Memorials near the main gate to see if the problem could be corrected. When he introduced himself there, the saleswoman smiled and said, "I know who you are, Dr. Konneker. You made it possible for our son to go to college." Her son, William Hardy, was a Cutler Scholar sponsored by Will and Ann Lee, majoring in computer engineering. Not surprisingly, Jack reported, "she assured Will it would be an honor to return a favor" by seeing that the markers were straightened. Two months later, the Konnekers were to receive photographs of the cleaned headstones resting on new concrete bases—and an invoice with a charge of "zero."

Back in town, the friends continued their tour, this time in areas where some of Will's memorable sites had changed or disappeared. "No longer was Penny's serving soda, nor the Davis Restaurant offering Cokes," Jack Pirozzi said. "Even the Diamond Grill had passed into memory. In fact, there wasn't any place in Greenfield to have a cool drink unless you went outside the business district to a fast-food place." Will noted that it would be a good place to open a Lion's Choice franchise, prompting immediate agreement by his friend. "I'll be happy to run it for you," said Jack, " if I can live on Second Street and walk to work."

At a pre-graduation dinner that evening, Will met Cutler Scholarship winner Elizabeth Cockerill and her parents. Later, he walked in the academic procession with the graduation class before presenting the scholarship. In his very brief remarks, he mentioned his affection for his town and university. Afterward, Jack stood aside and watched what he considered "a most heartwarming scene," as Will was "gracious and attentive to each of many persons who were genuinely pleased to greet him." On the drive to Columbus that night, Jack mentioned how proud Will must be of what he was able to do for his hometown. After a pause, Will said, "I always planned to do something for Greenfield; I just didn't know what it would be."

At midnight, after being on the go for more than sixteen hours, the two friends said goodbye in the lobby of their Columbus hotel. The next morning, an admittedly exhausted Jack Pirozzi flew home to St. Louis, but Will drove back to Ohio University for its commencement. Then he, too, flew from Columbus to St. Louis, where he underwent surgery to repair what proved to be a torn knee ligament, in time to accompany Ann Lee to Palm Springs, California, where she attended a Chi Omega board meeting, then to Olean, New York, for her sixtieth high school reunion. At a meeting of Ann Lee's former classmates, Will surprised her by announcing another Cutler Scholarship he had established in her name for Olean High School.

Early the next month, the Konnekers left home again, this time in the Rolls Royce, to attend the Lima, Ohio, wedding of Alicia Iseman, the second McClain High School Cutler Scholar and, by coincidence, the granddaughter of Dane Iseman, Will's close friend through grade school, high school, and college. From there, they headed for Chautauqua, detouring slightly to visit more ancestral graves along the way.

At the summer home, Will once again would attend the variety of Chautauqua programs, many of them with Ann Lee and Jane, work with the community's development board and its investment committee, keep attuned to Konneker Development and Ohio University projects by telephone and laptop computer, make some brief business trips, and join his wife in welcoming guests from various parts of the United States and abroad. But by his definition of relaxation, he would be following a relatively unstructured schedule—except for each early morning and late afternoon, when an insistent Trudy would use her Doberman wiles to lead him on long walks along the shorelines.

EPILOGUE

On September 27, 2002, Will and Ann Lee received a newly created award from Ohio University's College of Arts and Sciences. Named in their honor, the Wilfred R. and Ann Lee Konneker Award for Distinguished and Enduring Services was established to recognize individuals for sustained patterns of leadership and philanthropy.

In making the presentation, Arts and Sciences Dean Leslie Flemming noted that "Will and Ann Lee have demonstrated exemplary dedication to Ohio University for more than forty-five years. It seemed obvious that this type of exceptional service and support was deserving of a special award, and it seemed equally obvious that Will and Ann Lee be its first recipients."

B. Lynn, her husband, William Webster Jr., and their children, Cara and Trey, traveled from St. Louis for the program and weekend visits to several areas of the university, most of them conducted by former president Dr. Charles Ping, who continued to direct the Cutler Scholars program.

Among other guests at the awards dinner, and at an earlier reception, were students holding current scholarships sponsored by the Konnekers. One of the speakers, senior Rebecca Corbin, an integrated mathematics major, told what it meant to be a Cutler Scholar:

> My memories of the first time I met Dr. and Mrs. Konneker are still vivid. It was the night of my [McClain] high school graduation, almost four years ago, and I was attending the awards banquet held before the ceremonies. I was thrilled that my scholarship was going to be personally awarded to me by my donor. As I stood in the banquet hall, Dr. and Mrs. Konneker entered through one of the side doors. I had been given a description of them, but had not even seen their picture. However, their smiles welcomed me in a way that made me feel at ease, and, without waiting for a handshake or an introduction, Dr.

Konneker opened his arms and said "Congratulations," which almost brought me to tears.

From that day, Dr. and Mrs. Konneker have made so many opportunities available to me. For instance: canoeing the boundary waters of Minnesota and waking up each morning to the most breathtaking sunrise you have ever seen [Outward Bound phase]; walking into patients' rooms [at the Southern Ohio Psychiatric Hospital] and seeing them smile for the first time in days because they know you are there to spend time with them, not give them medication; working one on one with [DuPont] professionals designing projects to replace existing mechanical systems; and traveling to a foreign country [South Africa] to do student teaching.

These experiences have been so enriching to my life and my time at Ohio University that I will carry them wherever I go. Dr. and Mrs. Konneker have been very important in the shaping of my life, and will continue to be important well into the future after I graduate from Ohio University. I thank them from the bottom of my heart.

DOCUMENTATION

Most source materials for this biography were accumulated from interviews with family, friends, and colleagues of Wilfred and Ann Lee Konneker, and with other persons who, through various associations, were familiar with their lives and accomplishments. Supporting information was gleaned from newspapers, magazines, memoranda, catalogs, brochures, records, archives, news releases, Web sites, personal notes and letters, and official minutes of appropriate organizations. Several representatives of private, governmental, and educational institutions were kind enough to search records on behalf of the author. Multiple sources were used for verification of facts, dates, and figures throughout the manuscript. Some of these are identified by chapters in the following listing.

CHAPTER 2

Background information is from *An Ohio Reader,* edited by Dr. Thomas H. Smith (Grand Rapids, Mich.: William B. Eerdmans Publishing Co., 1975); *The Frontier in the Formative Years,* by Reginald Horsman (New York: Holt, Rinehart and Winston, 1970); Ohio Historical Society, *Ohio History* 84 (winter–spring 1973); *The Governors of Ohio* (Columbus: Ohio Historical Society, 1969); *Greenfield, Ohio: 1799–1999,* compiled by the Greenfield Historical Society, (Paducah, Ky.: Turner Publishing Co., 2000); *Encyclopedia of American History, Bicentennial Edition,* edited by Richard B. Morris (New York: Harper & Row, 1976).

CHAPTER 3

Histories, narratives, and statistical reports on World War II are so abundant it is difficult to attribute material to individual sources. Among the most helpful were *A History of National Service in America,* edited by Peter

Shapiro (College Park, Md.: Center for Political Leadership and Participation, 1994); and the *Encyclopedia of American History* (New York: Harper & Row, 1976). University records and interviews were supplemented by information in *The History of Ohio University,* by Thomas Nathanael Hoover (Athens: Ohio University Press, 1954); wartime issues of the student newspaper, the *Ohio University Post;* and *Athena* yearbooks.

CHAPTER 4

Information on Camp Fanin was gleaned from material from the Smith County Historical Society and Historical Commission, Tyler, Tex., and the Army Historical Foundation, Inc., Arlington, Va. Background on the Manhattan Project was found in *Atomic Quest,* by Arthur Holly Compton (New York: Oxford University Press, 1956); *Now It Can be Told,* by Leslie R. Groves (New York: De Capo Press, 1983); *Stone and Webster,* by David Neal Keller (Dover: Dover Litho Printing Co., 1989); and various magazines. Detailed information on the Dayton Project was contained in a booklet provided by a unit of the U.S. Department of Energy.

CHAPTER 5

Thomas T. Taber's *Sawmills among the Derricks,* vol. 7 of *Logging Railroad Era of Lumbering in Pennsylvania* (Williamsport, Penn.: Lycoming Printing Co., 1975) was one of several publications and interviews providing background on wood chemical plants. Some data on Ohio University in the mid- to late forties came from *The Baker Years,* by Paul Fontaine (Athens: Ohio University Press, 1961).

CHAPTER 6

Historical information about Washington University was gleaned from university publications and news releases, a Newcomen Society booklet containing a 1958 address by Chancellor Ethan Allen Hitchock Shepley, and *Washington University in St. Louis,* by Ralph E. Morrow (St. Louis: Missouri Historical Society Press, 1996). Data and observations on St. Louis were found in newspapers and magazines, including an in-depth feature by author Hamilton Basso in the October 1950 issue of *Outlook.*

CHAPTER 7

Although most information came from interviews, Nuclear Consultants Corporation records, reports, letters, and news releases were used to verify facts, figures, and dates throughout this chapter. Articles in St. Louis newspapers helped reinforce this verification.

CHAPTER 8

The Doberman Pinscher Club of America provided a wealth of information on the breed, training, and showing of Dobermans, as well as club activities. The *Ohio Alumnus* magazine recorded alumni activities in which the Konnekers took part. Mallinckrodt reports, in addition to announcements identified in the text, helped provide background for the merger.

CHAPTER 9

The Mallinckrodt profile and history were gleaned from company Web sites, news releases, and correspondence with the author. Company annual reports, memoranda, booklets, and media releases provided resources to reinforce material obtained through interviews. Information on the Eliot Society was reported in annual reports of Washington University in St. Louis.

CHAPTER 10

Information on schools was obtained from Principia in St. Louis; Mary Baldwin College, Stanton, Virginia; Culver Stockton College, Canton, Missouri. Special appreciation is extended to Ektelon company for providing extensive historical information about racquetball in the United States and abroad. Student unrest during the late sixties and early seventies was well documented throughout the nation's press and in various university reports, as well as having been observed by the author.

CHAPTER 11

Dates and figures on start-up of the Innovation Center were documented in a dissertation by Alan H. Geiger as a requirement for his Ph.D. in Philosophy in 1984 and through minutes of the Innovation Center and

Research Park Authority. Innovation Center publications provided some information on individual companies. Other sources are referred to in the text.

CHAPTER 12

Publications and correspondence were provided by St. Louis Opera Theatre, Powell Symphony Hall of St. Louis, Sheldon Concert Hall, and Center of Contemporary Arts (COCA) personnel. Minutes and official correspondence recorded some dates and facts of the Ohio University Foundation proceedings. Some Ohio University publications supplemented material gained from interviews concerning the Third Century Campaign. Several newspaper reports and personal letters were among materials describing the controversy and outcome of Dr. Konneker's brief service on the Ohio University Board of Trustees. Washington University in St. Louis provided data on his terms as a trustee there.

CHAPTER 13

Records in the Cutler Scholars Program office verified and supplemented information, most of which was gained through interviews, news releases, and publications. References concerning dedication of Konneker Research Laboratories are indicated in the text.

CHAPTER 14

General information on Battelle was obtained from Battelle Memorial Institute through its Webmaster.

INDEX

Page references in italics refer to the sections of photographs following pages 94 and 126.